THE OXFORD BOOK OF
CAROLS

THE
OXFORD BOOK OF
CAROLS

Percy Dearmer
R. Vaughan Williams
Martin Shaw

LONDON
OXFORD UNIVERSITY PRESS
NEW YORK TORONTO

Oxford University Press, Walton Street, Oxford OX2 6DP

OXFORD LONDON GLASGOW NEW YORK
TORONTO MELBOURNE WELLINGTON CAPE TOWN
IBADAN NAIROBI DAR ES SALAAM LUSAKA ADDIS ABABA
KUALA LUMPUR SINGAPORE JAKARTA HONG KONG TOKYO
DELHI BOMBAY CALCUTTA MADRAS KARACHI

Hardbound edition   ISBN 0 19 313104 8
Paperbound edition   ISBN 0 19 313120 X

First Published 1928
Twenty-Fifth Impression Re-engraved and Reset 1964
Thirty-First Impression 1977

Printed in Great Britain
at the University Press, Oxford
by Vivian Ridler
Printer to the University

CHORUS

well:
all: *Now let   good Christ-ians _ all be-gin An ho-ly   life to*

live,   And to re-joice and mer-ry be, For this is Christ-mas Eve.

3 Now for the blessings we enjoy,
    Which are from heaven above,
  Let us renounce all wickedness,
    And live in perfect love:
  Then shall we do Christ's own command,
    E'en his own written word;
  And when we die, in heaven shall
    Enjoy our living Lord:

    Now let good Christians etc.

4 And now the tide is nigh at hand,
    In which our Saviour came;
  Let us rejoice and merry be
    In keeping of the same:
  Let's feed the poor and hungry souls,
    And such as do it crave;
  Then when we die, in heaven we
    Our sure reward shall have:

    Now let good Christians etc.

In Davies Gilbert's West-country collection, *Some Ancient Christmas Carols*, 1822,
seven verses, with the first tune. The second tune is from Sandys, *Christmas Carols*, 1833.

3

1 CHRISTMAS EVE

SECOND TUNE

Traditional

Ibid.
(M.S.)

SOPRANO
ALTO

1. The Lord at first did Adam make Out of the dust and clay, And in his nostrils breathed life, E'en as the scriptures say. And then in Eden's paradise He placed him to dwell, That he within it should remain, To dress and keep it well:

2. Now mark the goodness of the Lord Which he to mankind bore; His mercy soon he did extend, Lost man for to restore: And then, for to redeem our souls From death and hellish thrall, He said his own dear Son should be The Saviour of us all:

TENOR
BASS

CHORUS

Now let good Christ-ians all be-gin An ho-ly__ life__ to live, And__

to re-joice and mer-ry__ be, For this is__ Christ-mas Eve.

3 Now for the blessings we enjoy,
    Which are from heaven above,
Let us renounce all wickedness,
    And live in perfect love:
Then shall we do Christ's own command,
    E'en his own written word;
And when we die, in heaven shall
    Enjoy our living Lord:

    Now let good Christians etc.

4 And now the tide is nigh at hand,
    In which our Saviour came;
Let us rejoice and merry be
    In keeping of the same:
Let's feed the poor and hungry souls,
    And such as do it crave;
Then when we die, in heaven we
    Our sure reward shall have:

    Now let good Christians etc.

In Davies Gilbert's West-country collection, *Some Ancient Christmas Carols*, 1822,
seven verses, with the first tune. The second tune is from Sandys, *Christmas Carols*, 1833.

5

2 A CHILD THIS DAY
(CHRISTMAS)

Traditional

Repeat CHORUS 𝄋

glad, poor sil - ly shep - herds–Why are you so dis - mayed?'
com - eth to all peo - ple by This ho - ly in - fant's birth':

may This bless - ed, This bless - ed, bless - ed day.

5. Then was there with the_ an - gel An host in - con - ti - nent Of
7. And as the an - gel_ told them, So to them did_ ap - pear; They

dim.

Repeat CHORUS 𝄋

hea - ven - ly bright sol - diers, Which from the High-est was sent:
found the young child, Je - sus Christ, With Ma - ry, his mo - ther dear:

6. Laud - ing the Lord our_ God, And his ce - les - tial King; All

(Two bass parts)

Now - ell, Now - ell, Sing all_____ we

Repeat CHORUS

ff Now-

Now - ell, Now - ell, Now - ell, } Now - - -
glo - ry be in pa - ra-dise, This heav'n-ly host did sing: }

may This bless - ed, This heav'n-ly host did sing. Now -

3. Silly—originally 'blessed' (*selig*), had still in the seventeenth century the meaning of 'simple'. Words and tune from William Sandys, *Christmas Carols*, 1833 (West of England). The usual seven out of twenty-one verses are here given.

7

3 SUNNY BANK
(CHRISTMAS)

Traditional

Ibid.
(M.S.)

SOPRANO
ALTO

1. As I sat on a sun - ny bank, a
2. I spied three ships come sail - ing by, come

TENOR
BASS

sun - ny bank, a sun - ny bank, As I sat on a
sail - ing by, come sail - ing by, I spied three ships come

sun - ny bank,⎫
sail - ing by, ⎭ On Christ - mas Day in the morn - ing.

3 And who should be with those three
But Joseph and his fair lady!   [ships

4 O he did whistle, and she did sing,
On Christmas Day in the morning.

5 And all the bells on earth did ring,
On Christmas Day in the morning.

6 For joy that our Saviour he was born
(that he was born, that he was born,)
On Christmas Day in the morning.

Cf. No. 18. Melody, with some of the verses, taken by Mr. J. H. Blunt, in 1916, from Mr. Samuel
Newman, at Downton, Wilts. 'A Sunny Bank' (either thus or as 'I saw three ships') is in most old
broadsides and modern collections. It has been found in the North, and West, and Midlands;
Cecil Sharp noted two versions, one in Worcestershire, and Bullen found it in Kent. There is an
early version in Forbes's *Cantus* (Aberdeen), 1666. We print the usual broadside version of this
form as given by Husk.

4 A VIRGIN MOST PURE
(CHRISTMAS)
FIRST TUNE

Traditional

Ibid.
(M.S.)

1. A virgin most pure, as the prophets do tell, Hath brought forth a baby, as it hath befel, To be our Redeemer from death, hell, and sin, Which Adam's transgression hath wrapped us in:

CHORUS

Aye and there - fore— be— mer - ry, re - joice and be you
and be you

mer - ry, Set— sor - rows— a - side; Christ—

Fine

Je - sus— our— Sa - viour— was— born on this tide.

VERSES 2-7

SOPRANO
ALTO

2. At— Beth - lem— in— Jew - ry a ci - ty there
3. But— when— they— had— en - ter'd the ci - ty so

TENOR
BASS

was, Where— Jo - seph— and— Ma - ry to - ge - ther did
fair, A— num - ber— of— peo - ple so migh - ty was

pass, And there to be___ tax - ed with ma - ny___ one
there, That Jo - seph and___ Ma - ry, whose sub - stance was

Repeat CHORUS 𝄋

mo', For___ Cae - sar ___ com - man - ded the same should be so:
small, Could find in ___ the ___ inn there no lodg - ing at all:

4 Then were they constrained in a stable to lie,
Where horses and asses they used for to tie;
Their lodging so simple they took it no scorn:
But against the next morning our Saviour was born:

Aye and therefore etc.

5 The King of all kings to this world being brought,
Small store of fine linen to wrap him was sought;
And when she had swaddled her young son so sweet,
Within an ox-manger she laid him to sleep:

Aye and therefore etc.

6 Then God sent an angel from heaven so high,
To certain poor shepherds in fields where they lie,
And bade them no longer in sorrow to stay,
Because that our Saviour was born on this day:

Aye and therefore etc.

7 Then presently after the shepherds did spy
A number of angels that stood in the sky;
They joyfully talkèd, and sweetly did sing,
To God be all glory, our heavenly King:

Aye and therefore etc.

2. mo'—more.
   Davies Gilbert, *Some Ancient Christmas Carols*, 1822. There is a printed version of 1734. Sandys (1833) prints a slightly different version with an eighth verse. Three versions are printed by W. H. Husk, *Songs of the Nativity*, 1868 (pp. 30, 56, 65). There are many tunes. The first we give from Gilbert; the second from Cecil Sharp's *English Folk Carols*, noted by him from Mr. Henry Thomas at Chipping Sodbury. The third was noted by Cecil Sharp in Shropshire, 1911, and printed in the *Journal of the Folk-Song Society*, vol. v., p. 24.
   For other 'Virgin Unspotted' tunes see Nos. 114 and 139.

4 A VIRGIN MOST PURE

(CHRISTMAS)

SECOND TUNE

Traditional

Ibid.
(M.S.)

1. A vir - gin most pure, as the pro-phets do tell, Hath
2. At Beth - lem in Jew - ry a ci - ty there was, Where

brought forth a ba - by, as it hath be - fel, To
Jo - seph and Ma - ry to - ge - ther did pass, And

be our Re - deem - er from death, hell, and sin, Which
there to be tax - ed with ma - ny one mo', For

A - dam's trans - gres - sion hath wrap - ped us in:
Cae - sar com - man - ded the same should be so:

And there-fore be mer-ry, set sor-rows a-side; Christ

Je-sus our Sa-viour was born on this tide.

3 But when they had entered the city so fair,
   A number of people so mighty was there,
   That Joseph and Mary, whose substance was small,
   Could find in the inn there no lodging at all:

   And therefore be merry, etc.

4 Then were they constrained in a stable to lie,
   Where horses and asses they used for to tie;
   Their lodging so simple they took it no scorn:
   But against the next morning our Saviour was born:

   And therefore be merry, etc.

5 The King of all kings to this world being brought,
   Small store of fine linen to wrap him was sought;
   And when she had swaddled her young son so sweet,
   Within an ox-manger she laid him to sleep:

   And therefore be merry, etc.

6 Then God sent an angel from heaven so high,
   To certain poor shepherds in fields where they lie,
   And bade them no longer in sorrow to stay,
   Because that our Saviour was born on this day:

   And therefore be merry, etc.

7 Then presently after the shepherds did spy
   A number of angels that stood in the sky;
   They joyfully talkèd, and sweetly did sing,
   To God be all glory, our heavenly King:

   And therefore be merry, etc.

2. mo'—more.
For note on this carol see p. 11.

4 A VIRGIN MOST PURE
(CHRISTMAS)
THIRD TUNE

Traditional

Ibid.
(R.V.W.)

Voices in unison (or solo)

ACCT.

1. A＿ vir - gin most＿ pure, as the＿ pro - phets＿ do
2. At＿ Beth - lem in＿ Jew - ry a＿ ci - ty＿＿there

tell, Hath＿ brought forth a ba - by, as＿ it hath be - fel,
was, Where＿ Jo - seph and Ma - ry to - ge - ther did pass,

To＿ be our Re - deem - er from death, hell,＿ and＿ sin, Which
And＿ there to be tax - ed with ma - ny＿ one＿ mo', For＿

A - dam's trans - gres - sion hath＿ wrap - ped＿ us in:
Cae - sar com - man - ded the＿ same should be so:

CHORUS

And— there-fore be mer - ry, set sor-rows— a - side; Christ

Je - sus our— Sa - viour was— born on— this tide.

3 But when they had entered the city so fair,
A number of people so mighty was there,
That Joseph and Mary, whose substance was small,
Could find in the inn there no lodging at all:

And therefore be merry, etc.

4 Then were they constrained in a stable to lie,
Where horses and asses they used for to tie;
Their lodging so simple they took it no scorn:
But against the next morning our Saviour was born:

And therefore be merry, etc.

5 The King of all kings to this world being brought,
Small store of fine linen to wrap him was sought;
And when she had swaddled her young son so sweet,
Within an ox-manger she laid him to sleep:

And therefore be merry, etc.

6 Then God sent an angel from heaven so high,
To certain poor shepherds in fields where they lie,
And bade them no longer in sorrow to stay,
Because that our Saviour was born on this day:

And therefore be merry, etc.

7 Then presently after the shepherds did spy
A number of angels that stood in the sky;
They joyfully talkèd, and sweetly did sing,
To God be all glory, our heavenly King:

And therefore be merry, etc.

2. mo'—more.
For note on this carol see p. 11.

5 THE PRAISE OF CHRISTMAS
(ADVENT: CHRISTMAS)

T. Durfey and others

Traditional
(M.S.)

1. All hail to the days that me - rit more praise Than
2. 'Tis ill for a mind to an - ger in - clined To

all___ the rest of the year,___ And wel - come the nights that___
think of small in - jur - ies now;___ If wrath be to seek, do not

dou - ble de - lights As well for the poor as the peer!___ Good
lend her thy cheek, Nor let her in - ha - bit thy brow.___ Cross

for - tune at - tend each mer - ry man's friend That
out of thy books ma - le - vo - lent looks, Both

doth but the best that he may, For - get - ting old wrongs with
beau - ty and youth's de - cay, And_ whol - ly con - sort with

ca - rols and songs, To drive the cold win - ter a - way.____
mirth and with sport, To drive the cold win - ter a - way.____

3 This time of the year is spent in good cheer,
 And neighbours together do meet,
 To sit by the fire, with friendly desire,
 Each other in love to greet.
 Old grudges forgot are put in the pot,
 All sorrows aside they lay;
 The old and the young doth carol this song,
 To drive the cold winter away.

4 When Christmas's tide comes in like a bride,
 With holly and ivy clad,
 Twelve days in the year much mirth and good cheer
 In every household is had.
 The country guise is then to devise
 Some gambols of Christmas play,
 Whereat the young men do best that they can
 To drive the cold winter away.

There is a black-letter copy of this wholesome song (of which twelve verses exist) in the Pepysian Collection. Rimbault preserved the tune. The first two verses are by Tom Durfey (1653-1723), the dramatist and friend of Charles II, in his *Pills to Purge Melancholy*, 1719.

6 IRISH CAROL
(CHRISTMAS)

Irish traditional

Ibid.
(M.S.)

1. Christ-mas Day is come; let's all pre-pare for mirth, Which
2. But why should we re - joice? Should we not ra - ther mourn To

(Bass) *Ding dong, ding dong, etc.*

fills the heav'ns and earth at this a - maz - ing birth. Through
see the hope of na-tions thus in a sta - ble born? Where

both the joy - ous an-gels in strife and hur - ry — fly, With
are his crown and scep-tre, where is his throne sub - lime, Where

Sop. {In
{Is

glo - ry and ho - san-nas, 'All Ho - ly' — do they cry,
is his train ma - jes-tic that should the — stars out - shine?

A.+T. *Ding*

heav'n the Church tri - um-phant a - dores with all her choirs, The
there no sump-tuous pa-lace nor a - ny inn at all To

dong, ding dong, ding dong, ding dong, ding dong, — ding — dong, ding

18

mi - li-tant on earth__ with hum - ble faith ad - mires. In
lodge his heav'n-ly mo - ther__ but in a fil - thy stall? Is

dong, ding dong, ding dong, with hum - ble_ faith__ ad - mires.
but in a __ fil - thy_ stall? Ding

(Bass) Ding dong, ding dong, ding dong, ding

hum - ble faith ad - mires. _____
in a fil - thy stall? _____

hum - ble_ faith__ ad - mires, with_ hum - ble_ faith_ ad - mires.
in a __ fil - thy_ stall, but__ in__ a __ fil - thy_ stall?

dong, ding dong, ding dong, ding dong, ding dong, ding dong.

3 Oh! cease, ye blessèd angels, such clamorous joys
   to make!
   Though midnight silence favours, the shepherds are
   awake;
   And you, O glorious star! that with new splendour
   brings
   From the remotest parts three learnèd eastern kings,
   Turn somewhere else your lustre, your rays elsewhere
   display;
   For Herod he may slay the babe, and Christ must
   straight away.

4 If we would then rejoice, let's cancel the old score,
   And, purposing amendment, resolve to sin no more—
   For mirth can ne'er content us, without a conscience
   clear;
   And thus we'll find true pleasure in all the usual cheer,
   In dancing, sporting, revelling, with masquerade and
   drum,
   So let our Christmas merry be, as Christians doth
   become.

The words and tune kindly communicated by Dr. Grattan Flood. The words in their original form were probably written for the tune in the seventeenth century, when Bishop Luke Wadding (1588-1657) wrote many hymns and carols for folk-tunes which had become associated with 'coarse' words. Since then carols of this kind have been traditional in Kilmore, South Wexford. Cf. No. 14.
   The English Carol (Routley) p. 218 gives alternative words by Anne Scott, 'Come ye thankful people'.

7 HEREFORD CAROL
(CHRISTMAS)

Traditional

Ibid.
(R.V.W.)

SOPRANO
ALTO

TENOR
BASS

1. Come all you faith-ful Christ-ians That dwell here on earth,
2. Be-hold the an-gel Ga-bri-el, In scrip-ture it is said,

Come ce-le-brate the mor-ning Of our dear Sa-viour's birth.
Did with his ho-ly mes-sage Come to the vir-gin maid:

This is the hap-py mor-ning, This is the bles-sed morn:
'Hail, blest a-mong all wo-men!' He thus did greet her then,

To save our souls from ru-in, The Son of God was born.
'Lo, thou shalt be the mo-ther Of the Sa-viour of all men.'

3 Her time being accomplished,
  She came to Bethlehem,
And then was safe delivered
  Of the Saviour of all men.
No princely pomp attended him,
  His honours were but small;
A manger was his cradle,
  His bed an ox's stall.

4 Now to him that is ascended
  Let all our praises be;
May we his steps then follow,
  And he our pattern be;
So when our lives are ended,
  We all may hear him call—
'Come, souls, receive the kingdom,
  Preparèd for you all.'

Collated (with the omission of several verses) from three sources: (1) Mr. Hirons, Haven, Dilwyn;
(2) Mr. Gallet, Leigh Linton, Worcestershire; (3) A ballad sheet published by R. Elliot, Hereford.
Melody from Mr. Hirons. From *Twelve Traditional Carols from Herefordshire* (Leather and Vaughan
Williams), Stainer & Bell.

8 SOMERSET CAROL
(CHRISTMAS)

Traditional

Ibid.
(M.S.)

1. Come all you wor - thy gen - tle-men That may be stan-ding by,
2. — Christ our bless - ed Sa - vi-our Now in the man-ger lay-
3. God bless the ru - ler of this house, And long on may he reign,

— Christ our bless - ed Sa - vi-our Was born on Christ-mas Day.
He's ly - ing in the man-ger, While the ox - en feed on hay.
— Ma - ny hap - py Christ-mas-es He live to see a - gain!

1,2) The bless - ed Vir - gin Ma - ry Un - to the Lord did say,
3) God bless our ge - ne - ra - tion, Who live both far and near,

1,2) O we wish_ you the com - fort and ti - dings of joy!
3) And we wish_ them a hap - py, a hap - py New Year!

Cf. No. 11. Taken from Mr. Rapsey of Bridgwater, by Cecil Sharp, *Folk Songs from Somerset* (No. 126), and *English Folk Carols*, No. XI (by permission of Novello & Co. Ltd.). Mr. Rapsey was taught the carol by his mother, and as a child used to sing it with other children in the streets of Bridgwater at Christmas time.

21

9 DARK THE NIGHT
(EPIPHANY: GENERAL)

Tr. K.E. Roberts

Melody by CANON OWEN JONES
Harmonized by Dr. CARADOG ROBERTS

1. Dark the night lay, wild and drea-ry Moaned the wind by Mel-chior's tower,
2. Now, Lord Je-sus, hear our call-ing, Deep the dark-ness where we stray;

Sad the sage, while pon-d'ring wea-ry O'er the doom of Ju-dah's power:
How shall we, mid boul-ders fall-ing, Know for thine the rough-hewn way?

When be-hold, the clouds are part-ed—West-ward, lo, a light gleams far!
Lo, a light shines down to guide us Where thy saints and an-gels are!

Now his heart's true quest has start-ed, For his eyes have seen the star.
Now we know thy love be-side us; For our eyes have seen the star.

A free translation of a Welsh carol by the Rev. W. Lloyd. The tune and
original Welsh words first appeared in *Carolan Nadolig* by Canon Owen Jones.

10 COME, LOVE WE GOD!
(CHRISTMAS: EPIPHANY)

Shann MS.

Ibid.

3 Three kingès came from the east country,
  Which knew they by astronomy,
    Et Balam vaticinia;
  They offered him gold, myrrh, incense;
  He took them with great diligence:
    Quam digna est infantia!

4 They turned again full merrily,
  Each came unto his own country:
    O Dei mirabilia,
  They had heaven's bliss at their ending,
  The which God grant us old and young.
    Deo Patri sit gloria.

1. *Regnante*, &c.—Now reigning in the sky. *O quanta*, &c.—O how great are these works.
2. *Cum*, &c.—With utmost reverence. *Quam*, &c.—How welcome are these gifts.
3. *Et Balam*, &c.—And by the prophecy of Balaam. *Quam*, &c.—How worthy is the infancy.
4. *O Dei*, &c.—O wonderful (works) of God. *Deo Patri*, &c.—Glory be to God the Father.
The tune and a selection from the partly illegible ten verses of the original are from 'Certaine
pretie songes hereafter followinge drawn together by Richard Shanne, 1611', in the MS. of the
Shann family of Methley, Yorks, now B.M., Add. 38599. Among various songs, some with music,
is this: it is headed 'A Christmas Carroll maid by Sir Richard Shanne, priest', who may have been
much earlier, since this has the characteristics of a fifteenth-century carol, and the tune is in a
style contemporary with the words. We have altered the error 'These kinges' in v. 3 to *Three*
(the number of course is legendary); 'and sence' to *incense*. V. 4 has 'younge', but the original
which Shann transcribed probably had 'ying'.

11 GOD REST YOU MERRY
(CHRISTMAS)

FIRST VERSION

Traditional
(usual version)

Traditional
(M.S.)

1. God rest you mer-ry, gen-tle-men, Let no-thing you dis-may,
2. In Beth-le-hem in Jew-ry This bless-ed babe was born,

For Je-sus Christ our Sa-viour Was born up-on this day,
And laid with-in a man-ger, Up-on this bless-ed morn;

To save us all from Sa-tan's power When we were gone a-stray:
The which his mo-ther Ma-ry No-thing did take in scorn:

CHORUS

O tid-ings, O tid-ings of com-fort and joy,

For

24

For Je-sus Christ our Sa - viour Was born on Christ-mas Day.

Je - sus Christ our Sa - viour Was born on Christ - mas_ Day.

3 From God our heavenly Father
    A blessèd angel came,
And unto certain shepherds
    Brought tidings of the same,
How that in Bethlehem was born
    The Son of God by name:

    O tidings, O tidings etc.

4 'Fear not,' then said the angel,
    'Let nothing you affright,
This day is born a Saviour,
    Of virtue, power, and might;
So frequently to vanquish all
    The friends of Satan quite':

    O tidings, O tidings etc.

5 The shepherds at those tidings
    Rejoicèd much in mind,
And left their flocks a-feeding,
    In tempest, storm and wind,
And went to Bethlehem straightway
    This blessèd babe to find:

    O tidings, O tidings etc.

6 But when to Bethlehem they came,
    Whereat this infant lay,
They found him in a manger,
    Where oxen feed on hay;
His mother Mary kneeling,
    Unto the Lord did pray:

    O tidings, O tidings etc.

7 Now to the Lord sing praises,
    All you within this place,
And with true love and brotherhood
    Each other now embrace;
This holy tide of Christmas
    All others doth deface:

    O tidings, O tidings etc.

12 GOD REST YOU MERRY

(CHRISTMAS: NEW YEAR)

SECOND VERSION

Traditional, London   Ibid.

SOPRANO
ALTO

1. God rest you mer-ry gen-tle-men, Let no-thing you dis-may, Re-
2. From God that is our Fa-ther, The bless-ed an-gels came, Un-

TENOR
BASS

-mem-ber Christ our Sa-viour Was born on Christ-mas Day, To
-to some cer-tain shep-herds, With ti-dings of the same; That

save poor souls from Sa-tan's power Which had long time gone a-stray,)
there was born in Beth-le-hem, The— Son of God by name.)   *And it's*

tid - ings of com - fort and joy, com-fort and joy: And it's

joy.

tid - ings of com - fort and joy, com-fort and joy.

joy.

26

3 Go, fear not, said God's angels,
   Let nothing you affright,
For there is born in Bethlehem,
   Of a pure virgin bright,
One able to advance you,
   And throw down Satan quite.
And it's tidings of comfort and joy.

4 The shepherds at those tidings,
   Rejoiced much in mind,
And left their flocks a feeding
   In tempest storms of wind,
And strait they came to Bethlehem,
   The Son of God to find.
And it's tidings of comfort and joy.

5 Now when they came to Bethlehem,
   Where our sweet Saviour lay,
They found him in a manger,
   Where oxen feed on hay,
The blessed Virgin kneeling down,
   Unto the Lord did pray.
And it's tidings of comfort and joy.

6 With sudden joy and gladness,
   The shepherds were beguil'd,
To see the Babe of Israel,
   Before his mother mild,
On them with joy and chearfulness,
   Rejoice each mother's child.
And it's tidings of comfort and joy.

7 Now to the Lord sing praises,
   All you within this place,
Like we true loving brethren,
   Each other to embrace,
For the merry time of Christmas,
   Is drawing on a pace.
And it's tidings of comfort and joy.

8 God bless the ruler of this house,
   And send him long to reign,
And many a merry Christmas
   May live to see again.
Among your friends and kindred,
   That live both far and near,
And God send you a happy New Year.

'God rest you merry', which is, as Bullen says, 'the most popular of Christmas carols', has two magnificent tunes, and deserves to be given in two versions.

The first version, No. 11, gives the best-known text, as in Sandys, 1833, accepting Bullen's correction of 'Whereas' in v. 6. Sandys gives 'friends' in v. 4, though we fancy that the alternative 'fiends' was the word more generally sung. 'God rest you merry' means 'God keep you merry', but the comma after 'merry' is generally misplaced. There is a version in the *Roxburgh Ballads*, vol. iii, c. 1770.

The second version, No. 12 (with the tune 'as sung', said Rimbault, a century ago, 'in the London streets'), we have reprinted from a broadside printed by J. & C. Evans, Long-lane, London, some fifty years before Rimbault. In this case we have reproduced the spelling and punctuation, only correcting the misprint 'comforts' in the first occurrence of the refrain; otherwise the carol is exactly as in the broadside, except that we have numbered the verses, and omitted some capital letters.

Rimbault stated that the tune printed by Sandys of the first version is from Cornwall.

The words of No. 11 can be sung to the London tune (No. 12), by singing 'O tidings of comfort and joy' twice for the refrain.

13 GOD'S DEAR SON
(CHRISTMAS : EPIPHANY)

Traditional

Ibid.
(M.S.)

1. God's dear Son with-out be-gin-ning, Whom the wick-ed
2. In Beth-le-hem, King Da-vid's ci-ty, Ma-ry's babe had

priests did scorn, ___ The on-ly wise, with-out all sin-ning,
sweet cre-a-tion; God and man en-dued with pi-ty,

On this bless-ed day was born; ___ To save us all from
And a Sa-viour of each na-tion. Yet Jew-ry land with

sin and thrall, When we in Sa-tan's chains_were_bound, And
cru-el hand Both first and last his power de-nied; Where

shed his blood to   do us good, With ma - ny a pur - ple bleed - ing wound.
he was born they did him scorn, And showed him__ ma - lice when he   died.

3 No kingly robes nor golden treasure
    Decked the birthday of God's Son;
  No pompous train at all took pleasure
    To this King of kings to run.
  No mantle brave could Jesus have
    Upon his cradle for to lie;
  No music charms in nurse's arms,
    To sing the babe a lullaby.

4 Yet as Mary sat in solace,
    By our Saviour's first beginning,
  Hosts of angels from God's palace
    Sounded sweet from heaven singing;
  Yea, heaven and earth, at Jesus' birth,
    With sweet melodious tunes abound,
  And everything for Jewry's King
    Upon the earth gave cheerful sound.

5 *Then with angel-love inspirèd,
    Three wise princes from the East,
  To Bethlehem as they desirèd,
    Came where as our Lord did rest:
  And there they laid before the maid,
    Unto her son, her God, her King,
  Their offerings sweet, as was most meet,
    Unto so great a power to bring.

6 Now to him that hath redeemed us
    By his precious death and passion,
  And us sinners so esteemed us,
    To buy dearly this salvation,
  Yield lasting fame, that still the name
    Of Jesus may be honoured here;
  And let us say that Christmas Day
    Is still the best day in the year.

In Gilbert (eight verses), with tune, 1822. A rougher version in nine verses is in *A Good Christmas Box*, Dudley, 1846. Here, as elsewhere, we have removed an accusation against the Jews.

14 WEXFORD CAROL
(CHRISTMAS)

English and Irish
traditional

Irish traditional
(M.S.)

1. Good peo-ple all,— this Christ-mas-time, Con-si-der well— and
2. The night be-fore— that hap-py tide, The no-ble Vir - gin

bear in mind What our good— God— for us has done, In
and her guide Were long time— seek - ing up and down To

send-ing his— be-lo-ved Son. With Ma-ry ho - - ly
find a lodg - ing in the town. But mark how all— things

we should pray To— God with love— this Christ-mas Day; In
came to pass: From e-v'ry door— re-pell'd, a - las! As

Beth - le - hem__ up - on that morn There was a bless-ed Mes- si - ah born.
long fore - told,__ their re-fuge all Was but an hum - ble ox-'s stall.

3 Near Bethlehem did shepherds keep
Their flocks of lambs and feeding sheep;
To whom God's angels did appear,
Which put the shepherds in great fear.
'Prepare and go', the angels said,
'To Bethlehem, be not afraid;
For there you'll find, this happy morn,
A princely babe, sweet Jesus born.'

4 With thankful heart and joyful mind,
The shepherds went the babe to find,
And as God's angel had foretold,
They did our Saviour Christ behold.
Within a manger he was laid,
And by his side the virgin maid,
Attending on the Lord of life,
Who came on earth to end all strife.

5 There were three wise men from afar
Directed by a glorious star,
And on they wandered night and day
Until they came where Jesus lay.
And when they came unto that place
Where our beloved Messiah was,
They humbly cast them at his feet,
With gifts of gold and incense sweet.

Kindly communicated, with No. 6, by Dr. Grattan Flood. The words (subsequently revised) and tune were taken down from a traditional singer in County Wexford. The words seem to have come from England: the first four and a half verses are in Shawcross's *Old Castleton Christmas Carols*, and the first verse was taken by R. Vaughan Williams from Mr. Hall, Castleton, Derbyshire (*Eight Traditional English Carols*, No. 7), with another tune. For another version see Sharp's *English Folk Carols*, viii.

15 WASSAIL SONG

(CHRISTMAS: NEW YEAR)

FIRST TUNE

North of England traditional

Ibid.
(M.S.)

1. Here we come a - was - sail - ing A - mong the leaves so
2. *Our was - sail cup is made __ Of the rose - ma - ry
3. We are not dai - ly beg - gars That beg from door to
4. *Call up the but - ler of this house, Put on his gol - den

green, __ Here we come a - wan - der - ing, So fair __ to be seen:
tree, __ And so __ is your beer __ Of the best __ bar - ley:
door, __ But we are neigh-bours' chil - dren Whom you have seen be - fore:
ring; __ Let him bring us up a glass of beer, And bet - ter we shall sing:

Love and joy come to you, And to you your was - sail
Love and joy come to you, And to

32

too, And God bless you, and send — you
you your was-sail too, And God send — you A hap - py New

Year, And God send — you A hap - py New Year.

SOLO

5.   We have got a lit - tle purse Of stretch - ing lea - ther
6.   *Bring us out a ta - - ble, And spread it with a
7. God bless the mas - ter of this house, Like - wise the mis - tress
8. Good mas - ter and good mis - tress, While you're sit - ting by the

skin; — We want a lit - tle of your mon-ey To line — it well with - in:
cloth; ___ Bring us out — a moul-dy cheese, And some of your Christ-mas loaf:
too; — And all the lit - tle chil - dren That round the ta - ble go:
fire, — Pray think of us — poor chil-dren Who are wand-'ring in the mire:

For Editors' notes see second tune, p. 35.

16 GOOD-BYE

17th century

GOD bless the master of this house,
 The mistress also,
And all the little children
 That round the table go:

  Love and joy, etc.

2 And all your kin and kinsfolk,
 That dwell both far and near;
I wish you a merry Christmas,
 And a happy New Year.

  Love and joy, etc.

15 WASSAIL SONG
(CHRISTMAS: NEW YEAR)

SECOND TUNE (LEEDS)

North of England traditional

Ibid.
(M.S.)

In each verse the three under parts sing the same words during the solo

34

too, And God bless you, and send you A hap—py New Year.

you,

SOLO

5.   We   have got   a   lit - tle purse Of stretch - ing lea - ther
6.   *Bring   us   out   a   ta - - ble, And spread   it   with   a
7. God bless the mas - ter of   this house, Like - wise the mis - tress
8. Good mas - ter and good mis - tress, While you're sit - ting by   the

skin; — We want a lit-tle of your mo-ney To line— it well with-in:
cloth; —— Bring us out— a moul-dy cheese, And some of your Christ-mas loaf:
too; — And all the lit - tle chil - dren That round— the ta - ble go:
fire, — Pray think of us poor chil-dren Who are wand - 'ring in the mire:

No. 16 might be sung to the second tune when the first tune is used for No. 15.

The starred verses are not suitable when the carol is sung in church, but they give a vivid picture of the Waits of old times. Text from Husk's *Songs of the Nativity*, 1868, where he refers to a Yorkshire copy of the carol in a broadsheet printed at Bradford as late as *c.* 1850, and to a Lancashire copy in a Manchester chap-book. The first tune from Yorkshire has been familiarized by Stainer. The second tune was learnt by Martin Shaw when a boy from his father, James Shaw, who had often heard it in the streets of Leeds in the eighteen-fifties; the Rev. J. T. Horton of Bradford reported some fifty years ago that it was still often sung by the Waits in the West Riding.

The charming seventh verse is also printed by Ritson in his *Ancient Songs and Ballads*, 1829, where he seems to have copied it from some source of the reign of James I or Charles I; he gives two verses only. Shakespeare may well have heard them sung outside his house on a Christmas night. We print them separately below, exactly as Ritson gave them, since they make a good conclusion to a carol-concert, and we have two tunes at our disposal:

16 GOOD-BYE

17th century

GOD bless the master of this house,
        The mistress also,
    And all the little children
        That round the table go:

Love and joy, etc.

2 And all your kin and kinsfolk,
        That dwell both far and near;
    I wish you a merry Christmas,
        And a happy New Year.

Love and joy, etc.

35

17 ALL IN THE MORNING
PART 1 (CHRISTMAS)

Traditional

Ibid.
(R.V.W.)

1. It was on___ Christ-mas Day,
2. *It was on___ New Year's Day, And all in the morn-

-ing, Our Sa - viour was born,___
They circum - cised our Sa-viour And our hea - v'nly___

King: *And was not___ this a___ joy - ful___

thing? *And sweet Je - - sus they called___ him by name.

Copyright, 1919, by Stainer & Bell Ltd.

3 It was on the Twelfth Day,
  And all in the morning,
  The wise men were led
  To our heavenly King:

  And was not this etc.

4 *It was on Twentieth Day,
  And all in the morning,
  The wise men returned
  From our heavenly King:

  And was not this etc.

5 *It was on Candlemas Day,
  And all in the morning,
  They visited the Temple
  With our heavenly King:

  And was not this etc.

36

17 ALL IN THE MORNING
PART 2 (LENT to EASTER)

Traditional

Ibid.
(R.V.W.)

6. It was on Holy Wednes-day,
And all in the morn-ing,
That Ju - das be - trayed
Our dear hea - v'nly King:
And was not this a woe - ful thing?
And sweet Je - sus we'll call him by name.

7.*It was on Sheer Thurs-day,
And all in the morn-ing,
They plaited a crown of thorns
For our hea - v'nly King:
And was not this a woe - ful thing?
And sweet Je - sus we'll call him by name.

8 It was on Good Friday,
And all in the morning,
They crucified our Saviour,
And our heavenly King:

And was not this etc.

9 It was on Easter Day,
And all in the morning,
Our Saviour arose,
Our own heavenly King;

The sun and the moon
They did both rise with him,
And sweet Jesus we'll call him by name.

The text has been completed from *Old Castleton Christmas Carols*, edited by the late Rev. W. H. Shawcross. Melody and first verse of text from Mr. Hall, Castleton, Derbyshire. From *Eight Traditional English Carols* (Vaughan Williams), Stainer & Bell.

37

18 I SAW THREE SHIPS
(CHRISTMAS)

Traditional

Ibid.
(M.S.)

SOPRANO
ALTO

1. I saw three ships come sail - ing in,
2. And what was in those ships all three? *On*
3. Our Sa - viour Christ and his la - dy.

TENOR
BASS

Christ - mas Day, on Christ - mas Day, And what was in those
Our Sa - viour Christ and

sail - ing in,
ships all three? *On Christ - mas Day in the morn - ing.*
his la - dy.

4 Pray, whither sailed those ships all three?

5 O, they sailed into Bethlehem.

6 And all the bells on earth shall ring,

7 And all the angels in heaven shall sing,

8 And all the souls on earth shall sing.

9 Then let us all rejoice amain!

Cf. No. 3, 'As I sat on a sunny bank'. In one or other version this is in all the broadsides, sharing its popularity with 'God rest you merry' and 'The Seven Joys'. The version above (in Sandys, 1833) differs only in v. 3 from the Derbyshire version with our first tune in Bramley & Stainer, *Christmas Carols New and Old*, 1871. A unique version introducing the Passion ('As I sat by my old cottage door') was taken down by Cecil Sharp in Worcestershire. Our second tune is from Sharp's *English Folk Carols*. There is another tune in the *English Carol Book*, Second Series (P. Dearmer and M. Shaw), Mowbray.

19 BOAR'S HEAD CAROL

(CHRISTMAS, Secular)

Queen's College, Oxford, version

Traditional
(M.S.)

1. The boar's head in hand bear I, Be-decked with bays and rose-ma-ry; And I pray you, my mas-ters, be mer-ry, *Quot es-tis in con-vi-vi-o:*

CHORUS

Ca-put a-pri de-fe-ro, Red-dens lau-des Do-mi-no.

End here.

2. The boar's head, as I un-der-stand, Is the rar-est dish in all this land, Which thus bedecked with a gay gar-land, Let us *ser-vi-re can-ti-co:*

Repeat CHORUS

3. Our stew-ard hath pro-vi-ded this, In hon-our of the King of bliss, Which on this day to be ser-ved is, *In Re-gi-nen-si a-tri-o:*

Repeat CHORUS

1. *Quot*, &c.—So many as are in the feast. *Caput*, &c.—The boar's head I bring, giving praises to God. 2. *Servire*, &c.—Let us serve with a song. 3. *In*, &c.—In the Queen's hall.
This version, as sung every Christmas at Queen's College, Oxford, is in Dibden's *Typog. Antiq.*, 1812, ii. 252, whence A. H. Bullen reprinted it in *Carols and Poems*, 1885 (p. 171), together with a version (p. 267) from Joseph Ritson's *Ancient Songs*, 1790 (from MS. Add. 5665 in the British Museum), the Wynkyn de Worde version correctly given with modern spelling (p. 170), and a quite different Boar's Head Carol (p. 172) sung at St. John's College, Oxford, in 1607. The carol in Hill's MS. (see No. 36) is a variant of the contemporary version of Wynken.

Jan van Wynken, of Worth, was Caxton's apprentice and successor: of his *Christmasse Carolles*, 1521, only the last leaf survives; it fortunately includes the colophon and is preserved in the Bodleian Library, Oxford: the text is reprinted with the original spelling in E. Flügel's *Neuenglisches Lesebuch*, 1895. Miss Rickert in *Ancient English Christmas Carols*, 1914, prints also three boar's head carols of the fifteenth century, but without references.

20 YEOMAN'S CAROL
(CHRISTMAS)

Church-gallery Book

Ibid.
(M.S.)

1. Let Christ-ians all with joy-ful mirth, Both young and old, both great and small,__ Now think up-on our Sa-viour's birth, Who brought sal-va-tion to us all: *This day did Christ man's soul from death__ re-move, With glo-rious saints to dwell_in heav'n a - bove.__*

2. No pa-lace, but an ox-'s stall, The place of his na-ti-vi-ty;__ This tru-ly should in-struct us all To learn of him hu-mi-li-ty:

3 Then Joseph and the Virgin came
  Unto the town of Bethlehem,
But sought in vain within the same
  For lodging to be granted them:
    This day etc.

4 A stable harboured them, where they
  Continued till this blessèd morn.
Let us rejoice and keep the day,
  Wherein the Lord of life was born:
    This day etc.

5 He that descended from above,
  Who for your sins has meekly died,
Make him the pattern of your love;
  So will your joys be sanctified:
    This day etc.

The words and tune are from an old church-gallery
tune-book, Dorset, and were discovered by the Rev. L. J. T. Darwall.

21 SIR CHRISTÈMAS
(CHRISTMAS, Secular)

c. 1500

Ibid.
(John A. Parkinson)

The two-part sections should be sung by soli, and the three-part sections by the full choir.

SOPRANO (or ALTO)

No - well, No - - - well, No - -

TENOR

No - well, No - - well,___ No - -

- well, No - - - well, No - - - - - - - - - - well.

- well, No - - - well, No - - - - - - - - - - - well.

SOPRANO (ALTO)

Who is there that sing - eth___ so,___ No -

TENOR I

Who is there that sing - eth so, No - -

TENOR II

Who is there that sing - eth so, No -

- well, No - - well,___ No - - - - - - - - well?

- well,___ No - - well,___ No - - - - - well?

- well, No - - well, No - - - - well?___

S. or A.

I am here, Sir Chris - te - - mas.___

T.

I am here, Sir Chris - te - - mas.___

41

The which caus - - - eth you for
Where - fore sing we all
And sing with us now

The which caus - - eth you
Where - fore sing we
And sing with us

to sing:
at a brayde: No - - - - - - well.
joy - ful - ly:

for to sing:
all at a brayde: No - - - - - - well.
now joy - ful - ly:

S. or A. No - - - - well. No - well, No - -

T. I No - - - - well. No - well, No -

T. II No - - - - well. No - well, No - -

- well, No - - - - well, No - - - - - - well.

- well, No - - - - - well, No - - - - - - well.

- well, No - - - - - well, No - - - - well.

Copyright, 1964, by Oxford University Press

2. more and less—great and small. 3. *Dieu, &c.*—God keep you, fair gentlemen. 4. brayde—to start, here 'all at once'. 5. *Buvez, &c.*—Drink well, through all the company.

Words and music from the MS. Add. 5665, which consists of English and Latin songs with music, dating probably from Edward IV to the early years of Henry VIII; this carol is attributed to Richard Smart, rector of Plymtree, Devon, from 1435-1477. The original pitch is a tone higher. See *Medieval Carols*, No. 80.

43

22 COVENTRY CAROL
(CHRISTMAS: INNOCENTS)

FIRST VERSION

Pageant of the Shearmen
and Tailors, 15th century

Original version of 1591

Lul - ly, lul - la, thou lit - tle tiny child, By by, lul - ly lul -

-lay, thou lit - tle tiny child, By by, lul - ly lul - lay.

1. O sis - ters too, How may we do For to pre- serve this day This
2. He - rod, the king, In his rag - ing, Char- ged he hath this day His
3. That woe is me, Poor child for thee! And e - ver morn and day, For

poor young-ling, For whom we do sing, By by, lul - ly lul - lay?
men of might, In his own sight, All young chil - dren to slay.
thy part- ing Neither say nor sing By by, lul - ly lul - lay!

The only surviving source of this carol is the rough facsimile of the 1591 manuscript published by
Thomas Sharp in his *Dissertation on the Pageants at Coventry* (1825), where it is found, together with
the Shepherds' Carol 'As I outrode' as part of the Pageant of the Shearmen and Tailors. This carol
gives added poignancy to the scene in which Herod's soldiers come in to slay the innocent children.
   In the original version the tenor part in bar 24 is written a third higher, but the whole copy is too
inaccurate for the resultant discord to be acceptable. For a discussion of these carols see *Monthly
Musical Record*, November 1959.

22 COVENTRY CAROL
(CHRISTMAS: INNOCENTS)

SECOND VERSION

Pageant of the Shearmen
and Tailors, 15th century

Modern version of tune
(M.S.)

REFRAIN *Not too slow*

Lul - ly, lul - la, thou lit - tle ti - ny child, By by, lul -

Fine

- ly lul - - lay.
1. O sis - ters too, How may we do
2. He - rod, the king, In his rag - ing,
3. That woe is me, Poor child for thee!

For to pre - serve this day This poor young - ling, ___ For
Char - ged he hath this day His men of might, ___ In
And e - ver morn and day, For thy part - ing Nei - ther

After 3rd verse, sing Refrain again

whom we do sing, By by, lul - ly lul - - lay?
his own sight, All young chil - dren to slay.
say nor sing By by, lul - ly lul - - lay!

D.S.

The text is that of Robert Croo, 1534, reprinted by E. Rhys, *Everyman and other Plays*. The Coventry plays were witnessed by Margaret, Queen of Henry VI, in 1456, by Richard III in 1484, by Henry VII in 1492, and we hear of the Smiths' play being performed in 1584, which brings us near to the date where the tune appears.
See the note on p. 44.

23 MAKE WE JOY
(CHRISTMAS: EPIPHANY)

15th century

Ibid.
(M.S.)

Make we joy now in this feast — In quo Chris-tus na-tus est: E - - - - - - - - - ya!

1. A
2. Ag -

Pa - tre u - ni - ge - ni - tus Through — a maid - en is come — to us: Sing we of him and

-nos - cat om - ne se - - cu - lum: A bright star made — three king - ès come, — For to seek with

D.S.

say   'Wel - come,— *Ve - ni   Re - demp - tor   gen - ti - - um.'*
their pre - sents— *Ver - bum   su - per - num   pro - di - - ens:*

3 *A solis ortus cardine,*
  So mighty a lord was none as he:
  He on our kind his peace hath set,
  Adam parens quod polluit:

4 *Maria ventre concipit,*
  The Holy Ghost was ay her with:
  In Bethlehem yborn he is,
  Consors paterni luminis:

5 *O lux beata, Trinitas!*
  He lay between an ox and ass,
  And by his mother, maiden free.
  Gloria tibi, Domine!

1. *In quo Christus*, &c.—On which Christ was born. *A Patre*, &c.—From the Father only-begotten. *Veni Redemptor*, &c.—Come, Redeemer of the nations (*English Hymnal*, 14). 2. *Agnoscat*, &c.—Let every age acknowledge (thee). *Verbum*, &c.—The celestial word proceeding (*E.H.*2). 3. *A solis*, &c.—Risen from the quarter of the sun (*E.H.*18). *Adam parens*, &c.—Which the parent Adam defiled. 4. *Maria ventre*, &c.—Mary conceived in her womb. *Consors*, &c.—Consort of the Father's light. 5. *O lux*, &c.—O blessed light, O Trinity (*E.H.*164). *Gloria*, &c.—Glory to thee, O Lord.
  Words (slightly altered in third lines of verses 1, 3 and 5) and melody from the Selden MS., B.26 (Southern English, *c.* 1450), which came to the Bodleian *c.* 1659. Facsimile and transcription in Stainer's *Early Bodleian Music*, and a more modern transcription in *Medieval Carols*, No. 26.

24 SUSSEX CAROL
(CHRISTMAS)
FIRST TUNE

Traditional

Ibid.
(R.V.W.)

VERSES 1, 2, & 4
Voices in unison

1. On Christ-mas night all Christ-ians sing, To hear the news_ the
2. Then why should men on earth be so sad, Since our Re-deem-er
4. All out of dark-ness we__ have light, Which made the an - gels

Harmony, *ad lib.*

an - gels bring, On Christ-mas night all Christ-ians sing, To hear the news the
made us glad, Then why should men on earth be so sad, Since our Re-deem-er
sing this night: All out of dark-ness we__ have light, Which made the an - gels

Unison

an - gels bring— News of great joy,_ news of__ great mirth,
made_ us glad, When from our sin_ he set_ us free,
sing_ this night: 'Glo - ry to God_ and peace_ to men,

Harmony, *ad lib.*

News of our mer - ci - ful__ King's birth.
All for to gain our li - ber - ty?
Now and for e - ver-more.__ A - men.'

48

VERSE 3

Melody and text from Mrs. Verrall, Monks Gate, Sussex. Other versions in *Journal of the Folk Song Society*, vol. ii, p. 127, and Cecil Sharp, *English Folk-Carols*, No. X. Arrangement for unaccompanied singing in *Eight Traditional English Carols* (Vaughan Williams), Stainer & Bell.

24 SUSSEX CAROL
(CHRISTMAS)

Traditional

SECOND TUNE

Ibid.
(R.V.W.)

1. On Christ-mas night all Christ-ians sing, To hear the news the an-gels bring__ News of great joy, news of__ great mirth,__ News of our mer - - ci - ful__ King's birth.__

2. Then why should men on earth be so sad, Since our Re- -deem - er made us glad, __ When from our sin he set__ us free, __ All for to gain our li - ber - ty?__

3 When sin departs before his grace,
  Then life and health come in its place;
  Angels and men with joy may sing,
  All for to see the new-born King.

4 All out of darkness we have light,
  Which made the angels sing this night:
  'Glory to God and peace to men,
  Now and for evermore. Amen.'

Tune noted by the late Dr. Culwick in 1904, from his mother, who had heard it many years previously in the streets of Dublin. The tune is printed in the *Journal of the Folk Song Society*, vol. ii, p. 126.

25 A GALLERY CAROL

(CHRISTMAS: EPIPHANY)

Church-gallery Book

Ibid.
(M.S.)

1. Re - joice and be mer - ry in songs and in mirth! O praise our Re - deem - er, all mor - tals on earth! For this is the birth - day of Je - sus our King, Who brought us sal - va - tion— his prai - ses we'll sing!

2. A hea - ven - ly vi - sion ap - peared in the sky; Vast num - bers of an - gels the shep - herds did spy, Pro - -claim - ing the birth - day of Je - sus our King, Who

3 Likewise a bright star in the sky did appear,
  Which led the wise men from the East to draw near;
  They found the Messiah, sweet Jesus our King,
  Who brought us salvation—his praises we'll sing!

4 And when they were come, they their treasures unfold,
  And unto him offered myrrh, incense, and gold.
  So blessèd for ever be Jesus our King,
  Who brought us salvation—his praises we'll sing!

The words and tune, from an old church-gallery book,
discovered in Dorset, like No. 20, by the Rev. L. J. T. Darwall.

26 SAINT STEPHEN
(DEC. 26 AND OTHER OCCASIONS)

Traditional

Ibid.
(M.S.)

SOPRANO
ALTO

TENOR
BASS

1. Saint Stephen was a holy man, En-
2. Before the elders was he brought His

-dued with heav'n-ly might, And many won-ders
answer for to make; But they could not the

he did work Be-fore the peo-ple's sight;
spi-rit with-stand, Where-by this man did speak.

And by the bless-ed Spi-rit of God, Which did his heart in-
Whilst this was told, the mul-ti-tude, Be-hold-ing him a-

(1.) He spa-red not, in e-v'ry place,
(2.) His come-ly face be-gan to shine

-flame,   1.) He spa-red not, in e-v'ry place,
-right,   2.) His come-ly face be-gan to shine } To

(1.) He spa-red not, in e-v'ry place,
(2.) His come-ly face be-gan to shine } Most

1.) He spa-red not, in e-v'ry place,
2.) His come-ly face be-gan to shine

52

CHORUS

preach God's ho - ly name: O man, do ne - ver
like an an - gel bright:

faint nor fear, When God the truth shall try, But mark how

But
But mark how

mark how Ste - phen, for Christ's sake, Was wil - ling for to die.
Ste - phen, for Christ's sake, Was wil - ling for to die.
But

mark how Ste-phen, for Christ's sake, Was wil - ling for to die.

3 Then Stephen did put forth his voice,
And he did first unfold
The wondrous works which God hath wrought,
Even for their fathers old;
That they thereby might plainly know
Christ Jesus should be he,
That from the burden of the law
Should quit us frank and free:

O man, etc.

4 'But, O,' quoth he, 'you wicked men!
Which of the prophets all
Did not your fathers persecute
And keep in woeful thrall?'
But when they heard him so to say
Upon him they all ran,
And then without the city gates
They stoned this holy man:

O man, etc.

5 There he most meekly on his knees
To God did pray at large,
Desiring that he would not lay
This sin unto their charge;
Then yielding up his soul to God,
Who had it dearly bought,
He lost his life, whose body then
To grave was seemly brought:

O man, etc.

Both the tune and words of this carol were preserved by Sandys, from whom we have taken the last two verses; the rest are exactly as in the older and slightly different version of Gilbert, but we have shortened the original, which is in eight verses.

53

27 THE FIRST NOWELL
(EPIPHANY: CHRISTMAS)

Traditional

Ibid.
(M.S.)

1. The first Nowell the angel did say Was to certain poor shepherds in fields as they lay; In fields where they lay, keeping their sheep, In a cold winter's night that was so deep:

2. They looked up and saw a star, Shining in the east, beyond them far; And to the earth it gave great light, And so it continued both day and night:

REFRAIN

Nowell, Nowell, Nowell, Nowell, Born is the King of Is - - ra - el!

†It is suggested that the organ remain silent until the refrain in one or more verses.

54

3 And by the light of that same star,
  Three wise men came from country far;
  To seek for a king was their intent,
  And to follow the star wheresoever it went:

  Nowell, etc.

4 This star drew nigh to the north-west;
  O'er Bethlehem it took its rest,
  And there it did both stop and stay
  Right over the place where Jesus lay:

  Nowell, etc.

5 *Then did they know assuredly
  Within that house the King did lie:
  One entered in then for to see,
  And found the babe in poverty:

  Nowell, etc.

6 Then entered in those wise men three,
  Fell reverently upon their knee,
  And offered there in his presénce
  Both gold and myrrh and frankincense:

  Nowell, etc.

7 *Between an ox-stall and an ass
  This child truly there born he was;
  For want of clothing they did him lay
  All in the manger, among the hay:

  Nowell, etc.

8 Then let us all with one accord
  Sing praises to our heavenly Lord,
  That hath made heaven and earth of naught,
  And with his blood mankind hath bought:

  Nowell, etc.

9 *If we in our time shall do well,
  We shall be free from death and hell;
  For God hath preparèd for us all
  A resting place in general:

  Nowell, etc.

ALTERNATIVE HARMONIZATION
FOR VERSES 3 AND 6 (MELODY IN TENOR)

55

As in Sandys, 1833 (except 'certain' for 'three' in v. I), with tune. Gilbert (1822) is rougher. The carol cannot be later than the seventeenth century. We have restored the verses omitted by Bramley in 1871, marking them with an asterisk: they are good, and will be sometimes very useful, for this carol makes a fine processional in the Epiphany season. Verse 2 is not quite historical: the carol is more for Epiphany than Christmas.

56

28 GREENSLEEVES
(NEW YEAR)

1642

Traditional
(M. S.)

Sopranos sing words

1. The old year now___ a-way is fled,_The new year it_ is
2. The name-day now___ of Christ we keep,Who for our sins did
3. And now with New___ Year's gifts each friend Un-to each o-ther

SOPRANO
ALTO

A.T.B. hum

TENOR
BASS

en-ter-ed, Then let us now_ our sins down-tread,_And joy-ful-ly all__ ap-pear:
of-ten weep; His hands and feet_were wound-ed deep, And his bless-ed side with a spear;
they do send: God grant we may all our lives a-mend,_And that_the truth may ap-pear.

All sing words

Let's mer-ry be this day,_ And let us now_ both sport and play:
His head they crowned with thorn,_ And at him they_ did laugh and scorn,
Now, like_ the snake, your skin _ Cast off, of e-vil thoughts and sin,

Hang grief,_cast care a-way!_God send you a hap-py New Year!__
Who for__ our good was born: God send us a hap-py New Year!__
And so__ the year be-gin:_God send us a hap-py New Year!__

A Waits' carol. There are three more verses, appealing to 'Jack, Tom, Dick, Bessy, Mary and Joan', and also to the dame of the house, rather pathetically pleading for good cheer. From *New Christmas Carols*, 1642 ('to the tune of Greensleeves'), in the unique black-letter collection of Antony à Wood, now in the Bodleian. We have had to alter some words for the sake of choral singing.

29 THIS NEW CHRISTMAS CAROL
(CHRISTMAS : EPIPHANY)

Traditional

Ibid.
(M.S.)

SOPRANO
ALTO

TENOR
BASS

1. This new Christ-mas ca-rol Let us cheer-ful-ly
2. Now the proud may come hi-ther And __ per-fect-ly

sing, To the hon-our and glo-ry Of our hea-ven-ly
see The most ex-cel-lent pat-tern Of __ hu-mi-li-

King, Who was born of a vir-gin, Bless-ed Ma-ry by
-ty; For in-stead of a cra-dle, Decked with or-na-ments

name; For poor sin-ners' re-demp-tion To the world_ here he came.
gay, Here the great King of glo-ry In a man-ger he lay.

58

3 As the shepherds were feeding
   Of their flocks in the field,
The sweet birth of our Saviour
   Unto them was revealed
By blest angels of glory,
   Who those tidings did bring,
And directed the shepherds
   To their heavenly King.

4 *When the wise men discovered
   The bright heavenly star,
Then with gold and rich spices
   Straight they came from afar,
In obedience to worship
   With a heavenly mind,

Knowing that he was born
   For the good of mankind.

5 *Let us learn of those sages,
   Who were wise, to obey.
Nay, we find through all ages
   They have honoured this day,
Ever since our Redeemer's

   Blest nativity,
Who was born of a virgin
   To set sinners free.

In Gilbert, 1822; in Sandys with tune, 1833. A new version, with the melody of the third phrase a tone lower, will be found in *The English Carol Book* (Mowbray's), No. 10.

30 LUTE-BOOK LULLABY
(NATIVITY)

W. Ballet (17th century)

Ibid.
(G.S.)

60

babe,'_____ sang she, 'my son, And eke a____
Sa - - viour born, Who hast vouch - saf - - ed from on
high To vis - it us that were for - -
To vis - it us,_____ us that were_ for - -
-lorn: La - lu - la, la - - lu - la, la - lu - la - by. Sweet babe,' sang
-lorn: La - lu - la, la - lu - la, la - - lu - la - by, Sweet babe,' sang
she, And rocked him sweet - - - ly___ on her knee.

From the MS. *Lute Book* by William Ballet, early seventeenth century, Trinity College, Dublin. B.M. Add. 17786-91 also contains a version for five voices or viols. We do not know that this Lullaby was ever in traditional use, but it belongs more to our First Part than to any other.

31 GLOUCESTERSHIRE WASSAIL
(CHRISTMAS AND NEW YEAR, Secular)

Traditional

Ibid.
(R.V.W.)

1. Was - sail, — was - sail, — all o - ver the town! — Our toast it is white, and our ale — it — is brown, Our bowl — it — is — made of the white ma - ple tree; With the was - - - sail - ing bowl we'll drink — to thee.

2. So here is to Cher - ry and to his right cheek, — Pray God send our mas - ter a good — piece of beef, And a good — piece — of — beef that — may we all see; With the was - - - sail - ing bowl we'll drink — to thee.

3 And here is to Dobbin and to his right eye,
   Pray God send our master a good Christmas pie,
   And a good Christmas pie that may we all see;
   With our wassailing bowl we'll drink to thee.

4 So here is to Broad May and to her broad horn,
   May God send our master a good crop of corn,
   And a good crop of corn that may we all see;
   With the wassailing bowl we'll drink to thee.

5 And here is to Fillpail and to her left ear,
   Pray God send our master a happy New Year,
   And a happy New Year as e'er he did see;
   With our wassailing bowl we'll drink to thee.

6 *And here is to Colly and to her long tail,
   Pray God send our master he never may fail
   A bowl of strong beer; I pray you draw near,
   And our jolly wassail it's then you shall hear.

7 *Come, butler, come fill us a bowl of the best,
   Then we hope that your soul in heaven may rest;
   But if you do draw us a bowl of the small,
   Then down shall go butler, bowl and all.

8 *Then here's to the maid in the lily white smock,
   Who tripped to the door and slipped back the lock!
   Who tripped to the door and pulled back the pin,
   For to let these jolly wassailers in.

Wassail, Wes hal, Old English, 'Be thou whole' (hale); a form of salutation, and hence a festive occasion. Cf. 'wassail bowl', cup, or horn.
   Cherry and Dobbin are horses. Broad May, Fillpail and Colly are cows.
   Sung by an old person in the county to R. Vaughan Williams. A variant was taken from Mr. William Bayliss at Buckland, Glos., and (5, 6, 7) from Mr. Isaac Bennett at Little Sodbury, Glos., by Cecil Sharp, *English Folk-Carols*, Novello. Collated with Sandys, &c. Other versions in Cecil Sharp's *Folk Songs from Somerset*, Nos. 128-30. Also found in Hone and in Chappell's *Collection of Anc. Eng. Melodies*. Brand recorded a hundred-and-sixty years ago that it was sung in Gloucestershire by wassailers carrying a great bowl dressed up with garlands and ribbon; Husk, that it was sung in 1864 in Over, near Gloucester, by a troop of wassailers from the neighbouring village of Minsterworth.

32 SOMERSET WASSAIL
(CHRISTMAS AND NEW YEAR, Secular)

Traditional

Ibid.
(M.S.)

PIANO
or
ORGAN

1. Was - sail,— and was - sail,— all o - - ver the town! The cup— it is white and the ale— it is
2. O mas - ter and mis - sus, are you— all with- in? Pray o - - pen the door— and let— us come

brown; The cup— it is made of the good— ash - en tree, And— so — is the malt of the best— bar - -
in; O mas - ter and mis - sus a - sit - ting by the fire, Pray— think up - on poor trav - 'llers, a - trav - 'lling in the

64

CHORUS

-ley: For it's your was - sail, and it's our was - -
mire:

-sail! And it's joy— be to you, and a jol - ly was-sail!

3 O where is the maid, with the silver-headed pin,
  To open the door, and let us come in?
  O master and missus, it is our desire
  A good loaf and cheese, and a toast by the fire:

       For it's your wassail, etc.

4 There was an old man, and he had an old cow,
  And how for to keep her he didn't know how,
  He built up a barn for to keep his cow warm,
  And a drop or two of cider will do us no harm:

       No harm, boys, harm; no harm, boys, harm;
       And a drop or two of cider will do us no harm.

5 The girt dog of Langport he burnt his long tail,
  And this is the night we go singing wassail:
  O master and missus, now we must be gone;
  God bless all in this house till we do come again:

       For it's your wassail, etc.

This Wassail was noted about twenty years ago by Cecil Sharp from the Drayton wassailers in
Somerset, and we print it separately because of its fine tune and distinctive words. Sharp thought
that the great dog of Langport was a reference to the Danes whose invasion of Langport is not
yet forgotten in that town.

33 WHILE SHEPHERDS WATCHED
(CHRISTMAS)

Nahum Tate

Traditional
(M.S.)

1. While shep-herds watched their flocks by night, All seat - ed on the ground, The an - gel of the Lord came down, And glo - ry shone a - round. 'Fear not,' said he (for migh - ty dread Had seized their troub - led mind); 'Glad ti - dings of great joy I bring To you and all man - kind.

66

2 'To you in David's town this day
    Is born of David's line
A Saviour, who is Christ the Lord;
    And this shall be the sign:
The heavenly babe you there shall find
    To human view displayed,
All meanly wrapped in swathing bands,
    And in a manger laid.'

3 Thus spake the seraph: and forthwith
    Appeared a shining throng
Of angels praising God, who thus
    Addressed their joyful song:
'All glory be to God on high,
    And to the earth be peace;
Good-will henceforth from
        heaven to men
    Begin and never cease.'

This carol, which is better known as a hymn because of its inclusion in all the hymnals, is here printed for the sake of the traditional tune proper to the words. It is, of course, now usually sung to 'Winchester Old' from *Este's Psalter* of 1592. The words first appeared in the *Supplement* to the *New Version*, the metrical version of the Psalms called 'Tate and Brady' by our forefathers, which appeared in 1696 and was 'allowed' by the King in Council, in place of the *Old Version* of 1556 ('Sternhold and Hopkins'); the earliest *Supplement* was in 1700 and contained 'While shepherds watched'; the *Supplement* of 1782 added 'Hark the herald' and four others. Soon after 1807, 'Jesus Christ is risen today' and 'Glory to thee, my God, this night' were added.

34 POVERTY
(NATIVITY)

Tr. K.E.Roberts

Welsh
(Dr. Caradog Roberts)

1. All poor men and humble, All lame men who stumble, Come haste ye, nor feel ye afraid;
2. Though wise men who found him Laid rich gifts around him, Yet oxen they gave him their hay: And Jesus in beauty Accepted their duty; Contented in manger he lay.

For Jesus, our treasure, With love past all measure, In lowly poor manger was laid.
3. Then haste we to show him The praises we owe him; Our service he ne'er can despise: Whose love still is able To show us that stable Where softly in manger he lies.

By permission of the Caniedydd Committee, Welsh Congregational Union.

A free translation of the Welsh Carol 'O Deued Pob Cristion'.

35 SANS DAY CAROL
(NATIVITY : PASSIONTIDE TO EASTERTIDE)

Cornish

Ibid
(M.S.)

1. Now the hol-ly bears a ber-ry as white as the milk, And
2. Now the hol-ly bears a ber-ry as green as the grass, And
3. Now the hol-ly bears a ber-ry as black as the coal, And
4. Now the hol-ly bears a ber-ry, as blood is it red, Then

Ma-ry bore_ Je-sus, who was wrapped up in silk:
Ma-ry bore_ Je-sus, who_ died on the cross:
Ma-ry bore_ Je-sus, who_ died for us all:
trust we our_ Sa-viour, who_ rose from the dead:
*And_*

Ma-ry bore_ Je-sus Christ our Sa-viour for to be, And the

first tree in the green-wood, it was the hol-ly, hol-ly, hol-

-ly! And the first tree in the green-wood, it was the hol-ly!

The Sans Day or St. Day Carol has been so named because the melody and the first three verses were taken down at St. Day in the parish of Gwennap, Cornwall. St. Day or St. They was a Breton saint whose cult was widely spread in Armorican Cornwall. We owe the carol to the kindness of the Rev. G. H. Doble, to whom Mr. W. D. Watson sang it after hearing an old man, Mr. Thomas Beard, sing it at St. Day. A version in Cornish was subsequently published ('Ma gron war'n gelinen') with a fourth stanza, here translated and added to Mr. Beard's English version.

36 THE SALUTATION CAROL
(NATIVITY: ANNUNCIATION)

15th century

Ibid.
(R.V.W.)

BURDEN

No-well, No-well, No-well, No-well! This is the sal-u-ta-ti-on of th'an-gel Ga-bri-el.

Fine VERSE

1. Tid-ings true there be come new, Sent from the Trin-i-ty By Ga-bri-el to Naz-a-reth, Ci-ty of Gal-i-lee. 'A clean mai-den, a pure vir-gin, By her hu-mil-i-ty Shall

2. When he first pre-sen-ted was Be-fore her fair vi-sage, In most de-mure and good-ly wise He did to her ho-mage; And said, 'La-dy, from heav'n so high, That Lord-es he-ri-tage, The

70

Repeat Burden

now con-ceive_ the Per - son Se-cond in de - i - ty.'____
which of thee_born would be I am sent on__mes - sage.__

3 'Hail, virgin celestiál,
    The meek'st that ever was!
Hail, temple of the Deity!
    Hail, mirror of all grace!
Hail, virgin pure! I thee ensure,
    Within a little space
Thou shalt conceive, and him receive
    That shall bring great soláce.'

4 Then bespake the maid again
    And answered womanly,
'Whate'er my Lord commandeth me
    I will obey truly.'
With '*Ecce sum humillima*
    Ancilla Domini;
Secundum verbum tuum,'
    She said, '*fiat mihi.*'

Salutation—an old name for the Annunciation. 2. demure—in its earlier sense of 'grave, sober'.
4. '*Ecce sum*', &c.—'Lo, I am the most humble handmaid of the Lord. According to thy word,'
she said, 'be it done to me.'
    Source: Bodleian Library, MS. Eng. poet e.i. (late 15th century) contains words and music for
one voice, transcribed in *Early Bodleian Music*, vol. II, p. 183. The words are also found in the Sloane
MS. 2593 and in Richard Hill's *Commonplace Book* (Balliol MS. 354), although these contain no music.
    Richard Hill's MS. has been printed (so far as the verse is concerned) by R. Dyboski for the
Early English Text Society, *Extra Series*, c. 1, 1908. It was discovered c. 1850, having been concealed
behind a bookcase for a great number of years. Our carols, Nos. 39, 118, 120, 169, 172, occur in it,
and other versions of Nos. 19, 38, 61 (and 184), 70, 116.
    Richard Hill was 'servant' or apprentice of John Wyngar, grocer, who became an alderman of
the City of London in 1493 and mayor in 1504. Hill married in 1518 Margaret, daughter of Harry
Wyngar, haberdasher. The earliest part of the book was written before 1504, the latest date in it is
1536; the carols seem all to have been transcribed together about 1504. This precious MS. contains
also English, French, and Latin poems, romances, extracts from Gower, &c., mixed with commercial
entries, tables of weights, prices, dates of fairs, medical and cooking recipes (including a 'medicen
for a doge that is poysent', and 'a good medycyne for a cutt' which begins 'Take a pynte of good
ale'), a form for making letters of attorney, a list of diaper table-cloths, &c. for the mayor's annual
feast at the Guildhall, rules for purchase of land, the bread assize, a treatise on wine, dates of his
children, pious ejaculations and reflections, notes on the breaking in of horses, the 'crafte to
brewe bere', forms for business letters in English and French, riddles, puzzles, with many humorous
and satirical verses.

37 THE ANGEL GABRIEL
(NATIVITY: ANNUNCIATION)

Traditional

Ibid.
(M.S.)

1. The an-gel Ga-bri-el from God Was sent to Ga-li-lee, Un-to a vir-gin fair and free, Whose name was called Ma-ry. And when the an-gel thi-ther came, He fell down on his knee, And look-ing up in the vir-gin's face, He said,—'All—hail, Ma-ry':

2. Ma-ry a-non looked him up-on, And said, 'Sir, what are ye? I mar-vel much at these ti-dings Which thou hast brought to me. Mar-ried I am un-to an old man, As the lot fell—un-to me; There-fore, I pray,—de-part a-way, For I—stand in doubt of thee':

CHORUS

Then sing we all, both

great and small, 'No-well, No-well, No-well'; We may re-joice to hear the voice Of the an-gel Ga-bri-el.

3 'Mary,' he said, 'be not afraid,
   But do believe in me:
The power of the Holy Ghost
   Shall overshadow thee;
Thou shalt conceive without any grief,
   As the Lord told unto me:
God's own dear Son from heaven shall come,
   And shall be born of thee':

   Then sing we all, etc.

4 *This came to pass as God's will was,
   Even as the angel told,
About midnight an angel bright
   Came to the shepherds' fold,
And told them then both where and when
   Born was the child our Lord,
And all along this was their song,
   'All glory be given to God':

   Then sing we all, etc.

5 Good people all, both great and small,
   The which do hear my voice,
With one accord let's praise the Lord,
   And in our hearts rejoice;
Like sister and brother, let's love one another
   Whilst we our lives do spend,
Whilst we have space let's pray for grace,
   And so let my carol end:

   Then sing we all, etc.

As in Sandys, 1833; Stainer gives the tune from Devonshire. The 'lot' in v. 2 is an allusion to the apocryphal Gospel of the Birth of Mary where Joseph is chosen out from the other suitors by the budding of his rod; the legend is introduced into the tenth play (Mary's Betrothal) of the so-called *Ludus Coventriœ*, and is familiar in pictures, e.g. in Raphael's *Sposalizio* in the Brera.

38 THE HOLLY AND THE IVY
(NATIVITY : LENT : AUTUMN)

Traditional

Ibid.
(M.S.)

VOICE

Solo (Soprano or Tenor)

1, 6. The hol-ly and the i - vy, When they are both full grown, Of＿
2. The hol-ly bears a blos-som, As white as the li - ly flower, And
3. The hol-ly bears a ber - ry, As red as a - ny blood, And
4. The hol-ly bears a prick-le, As sharp as a - ny thorn, And
5. The hol-ly bears a bark,＿ As bit-ter as a - ny gall, And

ORGAN
or
PIANO

all the trees that are in the wood, The＿ hol - ly bears the＿ crown:
Ma-ry bore sweet＿ Je - sus Christ, To＿ be our sweet Sa - viour:
Ma-ry bore sweet＿ Je - sus Christ, To＿ do poor sin - ners＿ good:
Ma-ry bore sweet＿ Je - sus Christ On＿ Christ-mas Day in the morn:
Ma-ry bore sweet＿ Je - sus Christ For＿ to re - deem us＿ all:

This carol may be sung with or without accompaniment

Cf. Nos. 35 and 63. Words and melody taken from Mrs. Clayton at Chipping Campden, Glos. (supplemented by words from Mrs. Wyatt, East Harptree, Somerset), by Cecil Sharp, *English Folk-Carols* (Novello). Another version is in Bramley and Stainer, and in the *English Carol Book* (Mowbray's) set to a French carol tune. 'Joshua Sylvester', in his *Christmas Carols*, 1861, was the first to publish the text in a collection; he took it from 'an old broadside, printed a century and a half since', i.e. *c.* 1710. Husk stated in 1868 that it was still retained in the broadsides printed at Birmingham. These two versions differ in the second line, 'Now are both well grown'. There is another carol of the Holly and the Ivy ('Holy berith beris') in Richard Hill's MS., another in the Harleian MS. ('Nay, Ivy, nay'), and others, for which Dyboski gives references. The subject is probably of pagan origin, and symbolized the masculine (holly) and the feminine (ivy) elements, as the tribal chorus developed into dialogue, all such songs being sung as a dance between the lads and the maids. 'The merry organ' occurs in Chaucer in the Nonne Preestes Tale: 'Chauntecleer's crowing had no peer— His voice was merrier than the merry organ/On mass-days that in the churche gon.'

39 THIS ENDRIS NIGHT
(NATIVITY)

15th century

Ibid.
(R.V.W.)

1. This en-dris night I saw a sight, A
2. This love-ly la-dy sat and sung, And

star as bright as day; And e-ver a-mong, a
to her child did say: 'My son, my bro-ther,

mai-den sung, 'Lul-lay, by by, lul-lay.'
fa-ther, dear, Why liest thou thus in hay?

FA-BURDEN

(M.S.)

3 'My sweetest bird, thus 'tis required,
   Though thou be king veray;
   But nevertheless I will not cease
   To sing, By by, lullay.'

4 The child then spake in his talking,
   And to his mother said:
   'Yea, I am known as heaven-king,
   In crib though I be laid;

   (*Fa-Burden*)

5 'For angels bright down to me light:
   Thou knowest 'tis no nay:
   And for that sight thou may'st delight
   To sing, By by, lullay.'

6 'Now, sweet son, since thou art a king,
   Why art thou laid in stall?
   Why dost not order thy bedding
   In some great kingès hall?

7 'Methinks 'tis right that king or knight
   Should lie in good array:
   And then among, it were no wrong
   To sing, By by, lullay.'

   (*Fa-Burden*)

8 *'Mary mother, I am thy child,
   Though I be laid in stall;
   For lords and dukes shall worship me,
   And so shall kingès all.

(*Fa-Burden*)

9 *'Ye shall well see that kingès three
   Shall come on this twelfth day.
   For this behest give me thy breast,
   And sing, By by, lullay.'

10 *'Now tell, sweet son, I thee do pray,
   Thou art my love and dear—
   How should I keep thee to thy pay,
   And make thee glad of cheer?

11 *'For all thy will I would fulfil—
   Thou knowest well, in fay;
   And for all this I will thee kiss,
   And sing, By by, lullay.'

   (*Fa-Burden*)

12 *'My dear mother, when time it be,
   Take thou me up on loft,
   And set me then upon thy knee,
   And handle me full soft;

   (*Fa-Burden*)

13 *'And in thy arm thou hold me warm,
   And keep me night and day,
   And if I weep, and may not sleep,
   Thou sing, By by, lullay.'

14 *'Now, sweet son, since it is come so,
   That all is at thy will,
   I pray thee grant to me a boon,
   If it be right and skill,—

15 *'That child or man, who will or can
   Be merry on my day,
   To bliss thou bring—and I shall sing,
   Lullay, by by, lullay.'

1. This endris—('thys ender' in the MS. Add. 31922, 'this endurs' in the MS., Advocates' Lib., Edinburgh), the other night, a few nights ago.   ever among—every now and then.   3. veray—true. 5. light—alight.   no nay—not to be denied.   10. pay—satisfaction.   11. fay—faith.   14. skill— reasonable.
   Was not new when it was written out in the Bodleian MS., Eng. Poet., e. 1, which is dated between 1460 and 1490. It is in the MS. of Richard Hill, the grocer (cf. No. 36). Four versions are given by Dyboski in the Early English Text Society, Extra Series, c. 1, p. 174. Wright's version, from the Sloane MS. 2593 (see nos. 174, 182), Percy Society, 1841, is reprinted in Julian's *Dictionary of Hymnology* (p. 209) by Helmore. Two of the versions are in Chambers and Sidgwick, pp. 119 and 121. The tune is used in the *English Hymnal* (20) and *Songs of Praise* (72): it is in the fifteenth or sixteenth century MS., B.M., Royal Appendix 58, set for three voices, with melody in the tenor.

40 WONDER TIDINGS
(NATIVITY)

15th century

Ibid.
(School of J. Dunstable)
(M.S.)

What ti - dings bring-est thou, mes - sen - ger, Of Chris-tes

birth this jol-ly___ day? 1. A babe is born of high__ na - ture,
2. A won - der thing is now__ be - fall;

The Prince of peace that e - ver shall be; Of heav'n and earth he
That King that form - ed star__ and sun, Hea - ven and earth and

hath__ the cure: His lord - ship is e - ter - ni - ty: Such
an - gels all, Now in man - kind is new__ be - gun: Such

won - der ti - dings ye — may hear, That man is made now
won - der ti - dings ye — may hear, An in - fant now of

God - des peer, Whom sin had made — but fien - des prey.
but — one year, That hath been e - ver and shall — be ay.

3 That seemeth strange to us to see,
    This bird that hath this babe yborn
And Lord conceived of high degree
    A maiden is, as was beforn:
        Such wonder tidings ye may hear,
        That maiden and mother is one in fere,
        And she a lady of great array.

4 That loveliest gan greet her child,
    'Hail, son! Hail, brother! Hail, father dear!'
'Hail, daughter! Hail, sister! Hail, mother mild!'
    This hailing was on quaint mannere:
        Such wonder tidings ye may hear,
        That hailing was of so good cheer
        That mannés pain is turned to play.

1. cure—charge. 3. bird—girl. beforn—before. in fere—together. 4. quaint—(from 'coint', 'cognitus', 'known'), had several shades of meaning in the fifteenth century—'strange', 'curiously wrought', 'dainty', 'graceful'.
Words and tune from a MS. at Cambridge (T.C.C., O.3.58). Another version from a Bodleian MS. is printed in Stainer's *Early Bodleian Music*, vol. 2, p. 125. Accurate transcriptions of both versions are to be found in *Medieval Carols*, Nos. 11 and 27, (Greene, No. 117); in both cases the chorus repeat the opening phrase 'What tidings bringest thou, messenger' at the point marked *. There is no evidence for the ascription to Dunstable. In this carol an opening challenge is preserved, both in words and music. We can imagine, with Sir Edmund Chambers, how 'the chanted question comes nearer and nearer along the crooked medieval street': or we can picture a company singing in a hall round the crackling yule logs; the door opens, and the Messenger enters; the company sings 'What tidings . . .', and the Messenger answers with the first stanza, and a choir perhaps takes up the refrain, which changes as the tidings are told out. The same might be done today in a parish hall; or in church, the Messenger, wearing a gown and carrying a staff, like a verger, might walk up the middle alley, the choir beginning 'What tidings' as he approaches the chancel. He would proceed as far as the midst of the chancel, and then, turning west, would sing his verses.

41 RIGHTEOUS JOSEPH
(NATIVITY: ADVENT)

Cornish

Ibid. (M.S.)

1. When right-eous Jo - seph wed - ded was To
'Hail, bless - ed Ma - ry, full _ of grace, The
CHORUS: *Then sing you all, _ both great_ and small, No -*

Is - rael's He - brew maid, The an - gel _ Gab - riel
Lord re - main on thee; Thou shalt con - ceive and
- well, No - well, No - well! We may re - joice to

came from heav'n, And to _ the Vir - gin said:
bear a son, Our Sa - viour for to be':
hear the voice Of the an - gel Gab - ri - el.

2 *Then Joseph thought to shun all shame
　And Mary to forsake;
But God's dear angel in a dream
　His mind did undertake:
'Fear not, old Joseph, she's thy wife,
　She's still a spotless maid;
There's no conceit or sin at all
　Against her can be laid':

　　　　Then sing etc.

3 Thus Mary and her husband kind
　Together did remain,
Until the time of Jesus' birth,
　As scripture doth make plain.
As mother, wife, and virtuous maid,
　Our Saviour sweet conceived;
And in due time to bring us him,
　Of whom we were bereaved:

　　　　Then sing etc.

4 Sing praises all, both young and old,
　To him that wrought such things;
And all without the means of man,
　Sent us the King of kings,
Who is of such a spirit blest,
　That with his might did quell
The world, the flesh, and by his death
　Did conquer death and hell:

　　　　Then sing etc.

As in Davies Gilbert, 1822 (with seven verses); but v. 2 from the less corrupt version of Miss Hocking. The tune has been kindly communicated by the Rev. G. H. Doble, who noted it from Elizabeth Hocking, at Redruth, Cornwall. Miss Hocking was then 84 (1920), and had learnt it from her mother as a very small child, i.e. *c.* 1840.

42 REMEMBER
(LENT: CHRISTMAS)

Melismata, 1611

Ibid.
(Thomas Ravenscroft, 1611)

1. Re - mem - ber,   O   thou man,   O   thou man,   O   thou man,
2.*Re - mem - ber   God's   good-ness,   O   thou man,   O   thou man,

Re - mem - ber,   O   thou man, Thy   time   is   spent: Re-mem-ber,   O   thou man,
Re - mem - ber   God's   good-ness And   pro-mise   made: Re-mem-ber   God's   good-ness,

How thou   cam'st   to   me then, And   I   did   what   I   can, There-fore re - pent.
How his   on - ly   Son   he sent, Our   sins   for   to   re-dress: Be   not a - fraid.

3 The angels all did sing,
    O thou man, O thou man,
  The angels all did sing,
    On Sion hill:
  The angels all did sing
  Praises to our heavenly King,
  And peace to man living,
    With right good will.

4 To Bethlem did they go,
    O thou man, O thou man,
  To Bethlem did they go,
    This thing to see:
  To Bethlem did they go,
  To see whether it was so,
  Whether Christ was born or no
    To set us free.

5 In Bethlem was he born,
    O thou man, O thou man,
  In Bethlem was he born,
    For mankind dear:
  In Bethlem was he born
  For us that were forlorn,
  And therefore took no scorn,
    Our sins to bear,

6 Give thanks to God always,
    O thou man, O thou man,
  Give thanks to God always,
    With hearts most jolly:
  Give thanks to God always
  Upon this blessèd day;
  Let all men sing and say,
    Holy, holy.

The words, which are probably of the sixteenth century, are set to music in Ravenscroft's *Melismata*.
Four verses omitted will be found in Bullen. Mr. Thomas Hardy gives another version in *Under
the Greenwood Tree*. For Lent, vv. 1, 2, 3, 5 are suitable.

43 THE SEVEN VIRGINS
(THE PASSION)

Traditional

Ibid.
(R. V. W.)

1. All___ un - der the leaves, the___ leaves_ of life, I
2. 'O___ what are you seek - ing, you sev - en fair maids, All
3. 'We're_ seek - ing___ for no___ leaves,_ Tho - mas, But

met with_ vir - gins_ sev'n, And_ one_ of them was
un - der the leaves of_ life?_ Come_ tell,_ come tell me
for a _ friend of_ thine; We're_ seek - ing for sweet

Ma - ry mild, Our___ Lord's mo - ther_ from_ heav'n.
what seek you All___ un - der the leaves_ of _ life.'
Je - sus Christ, To___ be_ our_ guide_ and_ thine.'

4 'Go you down, go you down to yonder town,
    And sit in the gallery;
And there you'll find sweet Jesus Christ,
    Nailed to a big yew-tree.'

5 So down they went to yonder town,
    As fast as foot could fall,
And many a grievous bitter tear,
    From the virgins' eyes did fall.

6 'O peace, mother, O peace, mother,
    Your weeping doth me grieve;
O I must suffer this,' he said,
    'For Adam and for Eve.'

7 'O how can I my weeping leave,
    Or my sorrows undergo,
Whilst I do see my own Son die,
    When sons I have no mo'?'

8 'Dear mother, dear mother, you must take John,
    All for to be your son,
And he will comfort you sometimes,
    Mother, as I have done.'

9 'O, come, thou John Evangelist,
    Thou'rt welcome unto me,
But more welcome my own dear son,
    That I nursed upon my knee.'

10 Then he laid his head on his right shoulder,
    Seeing death it struck him nigh:
'The Holy Ghost be with your soul,—
    I die, mother dear, I die.'

11 Oh the rose, the rose, the gentle rose,
    And the fennel that grows so green!
God give us grace in every place,
    To pray for our king and queen.

12 Furthermore for our enemies all
    Our prayers they should be strong.
Amen, Good Lord! your charity
    Is the ending of my song.

Melody and a version of text from Mrs. Whatton and Mrs. Loveridge, The Homme, Dilwyn. From *Twelve Traditional Carols from Herefordshire* (Leather and Vaughan Williams), Stainer & Bell. Cf. *Popular Carols*, by F. Sidgwick (Sidgwick & Jackson). This fine example of the way in which a mystical vision is created by the best folk-poetry appeared in the Staffordshire *A Good Christmas Box*, 1847. Sylvester (1861) printed a version of it from an 'old Birmingham broadside'. Sir A. Quiller-Couch included it in the *Oxford Book of English Verse*, and Walter de la Mare in *Come Hither*.

44 THE LAMB OF GOD
(THE PASSION: EASTER: NEW YEAR)

Traditional

Ibid.
(M.S.)

1. A - wake, a - wake, ye drow - sy souls, And
2. They bound Christ's bo - dy to a tree, And

hear what I shall tell; Re - mem - ber Christ, the
woun - ded him full sore; From ev - 'ry wound the

Lamb of God, Re - deem'd our souls from hell. He's
blood ran down, Till Christ could bleed no more; His

crowned with thorns, spit on with scorn, His friends have hid them-
dy - ing wounds, all rent and tore, Were co - vered with pear - ly

CHORUS

- selves: *So God send you all much joy in the year, in the*
gore:

84

year, So God send you all— much— joy—— in— the year.

3 And when his foes had murdered Christ
And shown their cruel spite,
The sun and moon did hide their heads
And went in mourning straight;
The heavens stood amazed, and angels gazed,
And the earth was darkened quite:

So God send you etc.

4 *And when Christ's soul departed
And from his body fled,
The rocks did rend, the graves did ope,
And then appeared the dead;
All they that were there did quake for fear–
'Twas the Son of God', they said:

So God send you etc.

PART 2 (EASTER, ETC.)

5 It was early in the morning
That Mary did him seek;
She saw two angels sitting
At Jesus' head and feet:
Mary shed tears while Christ appeared,
And he said: 'Why dost thou weep?'

So God send you etc.

6 Then Christ he called Thomas,
And bid him: 'Come and see,
And put thy fingers in the wounds
That are in my body;
And be not faithless, but believe,
And happy shalt thou be':

So God send you etc.

7 Then Christ called his disciples,
Divided by his death,
And said: 'All powers are given to you
In heaven and on earth;
Go forth and teach all nations;
Despise them not,' he saith:

So God send you etc.

8 *'Go seek you every wandering sheep
That doth on earth remain,
Till I myself have paid your debts
And turned you back again;
Come all ye heavy laden,
I'll ease you of your pain':

So God send you etc.

PART 3 (GOOD WISHES)

9 *God bless the ruler of this house
And send him long to reign;
Let many a good and happy year
Go over his head again,
And all his godly family
That serveth the Lord so dear:

So God send you etc.

10 *God bless the mistress of this house,
With peace unto her breast,
And, let her body be asleep or awake,
Lord, send her soul to rest,
And all her godly family
That serveth the Lord so dear:

So God send you etc.

The melody and the first and last verses were taken down by Cecil Sharp at Donnington Wood,
Shropshire; the refrain as noted was 'So God send you all a joyful New Year', and v. 5 comes
after v. 8. We have substituted 'friends' in v. 1 and 'foes' in v. 3 for 'Jews'; vv. 4 and 7 seem to be
corrupt in the original, and we have slightly amended them. The carol is printed in *A Good Christmas
Box*, 1847, and in an undated chap-book printed by J. Bates, New Town, Bilston. It is given in
Cecil Sharp's *English Folk-Carols*, and is evidently a Passiontide and Easter carol, not perfectly
remembered, and adapted to the Christmas-Epiphany season to which carol-singing came to
be restricted.

45 SUSSEX MUMMERS' CAROL
(LENT: THE PASSION)

Traditional

Ibid.
(L.E.B.)

1. O_ mor-tal man, re - mem-ber well, When Christ our Lord was__ born,___ He was cru - ci - fied_ be - tween two_ thieves, And crown-ed with the thorn,_ And crown - - ed_ with_____ the thorn.

2. O_ mor-tal man, re - mem-ber well, When Christ died on_ the__ rood,___ 'Twas for our sins _ and_ wick - ed_ ways_ Christ shed his pre-cious blood,_ Christ shed_____ his_ pre - - - cious blood.

3 O mortal man, remember well,
   When Christ was wrapped in clay,
He was taken to a sepulchre
   Where no man ever lay.

4 *God bless the mistress of this house
   With gold chain round her breast;
Where'er her body sleeps or wakes,
   Lord, send her soul to rest.

5 *God bless the master of this house
   With happiness beside;
Where'er his body rides or walks
   Lord Jesus be his guide.

6 God bless your house, your children too,
   Your cattle and your store;
The Lord increase you day by day,
   And send you more and more.

Sung by Christmas Mummers from the neighbourhood of Horsham, c. 1876-81. Collected by Lucy E. Broadwood. See Broadwood's *Sussex Songs* (Stanley Lucas and Weber, later Leonard & Co.); L. E. Broadwood's *English Traditional Songs and Carols* (Boosey & Co.) and her *Christmas Carols for Children* (A. and C. Black), in all of which the original opening verse, describing the Annunciation, is retained.

ALTERNATIVE HARMONIZATION

1. O — mor - tal man, re - - mem - ber well, When —
2. O — mor - tal man, re - - mem - ber well, When —

Christ our Lord was — born, — He was cru - ci - fied — be -
Christ died on the — rood, — 'Twas — for our sins — and —

-tween two — thieves, And crown - ed with the — thorn, — And
wick - ed — ways — Christ shed his pre - cious — blood, — Christ

crown - - - ed — with the thorn.
shed — his — pre - - - cious blood.

For unison setting of last verse see overleaf.

87

UNISON SETTING FOR LAST VERSE

(R.V.W.)

6. God bless your house, your chil-dren too, Your cat-tle and your store; The Lord in-crease you day by day, And send you more and more, And send you more and more.

46 THE BELLMAN'S SONG
(GENERAL: THE PASSION)

FIRST TUNE

Traditional

Ibid.
(M.S.)

VERSES 1, 2

1. The moon shines bright, and the stars give a light: A
2. A-wake, a-wake, good people all; A--

lit-tle be-fore it was day Our Lord, our God, he
-wake, and you shall hear, Our Lord, our God, died

called on us, And bid us a-wake and pray.
on the cross For us whom he loved so dear.

VERSES 3, 5

3. O fair, O fair Je - - ru - sa - lem, When
5. And for the sav - ing of our souls Christ

shall I come to thee? When shall my sor - rows
died up - on the cross; We ne'er shall do for

TENOR { When
       { We

[Bass: words as for S. and A.]

have an end, Thy joy that I may see?
Je - sus Christ As he hath done for us.
shall my sor - rows end, that I may see.
ne'er shall do for Christ as he for us.

VERSES 4,6

4. The fields were green as — green could be, When
6. The life of man is — but a — span And

from his glo-rious seat Our — Lord, our — God, he—
cut down in its flower; We are here to-day, and to-

wa-tered us, With his heav'n-ly dew— so— sweet.
-mor-row are gone, The— crea-tures of— an— hour.

This carol is common in the old broadsides, and some of its verses have strayed into other folk-carols (e.g. into the May Carol from Hertfordshire, printed in Hone's *Every-day Book*, 1821, cf. No. 47). The longer version, in ten verses, is printed by Sandys, Husk, Bullen and others; it includes the 'With one turf' verse, and concludes with New Year wishes (like those of No. 47, with 'here' and 'Year' instead of 'stay' and 'May'); but the song is clearly a Passion carol or Atonement carol, of the type that became common in the later carol era. We have used Husk's form of v. 6. V. 3 is a variant of the first verse of 'Jerusalem, my happy home' (see No. 132), the twenty-six verses of which are in the *English Hymnal* and *Songs of Praise*. The first tune has been familiar since its publication by Bramley & Stainer in 1871. It might perhaps be some version of this carol to which Shakespeare refers in the page's song, 'It was a lover and his lass', in *As You Like It*—

This carol they began that hour,
With a hey, and a ho, and a hey nonino,
How that a life was but a flower,
In the spring time, the only pretty ring time.

91

46 THE BELLMAN'S SONG
(GENERAL: THE PASSION)
SECOND TUNE

Traditional

Ibid.
(R.V.W.)

VOICES
IN UNISON

ORGAN
or
PIANO

1. The moon shines bright, and the stars give a light: A
2. A - wake, a - wake, good people all; A -

lit - tle be - fore it was day   Our Lord, our God, he
-wake, and you shall hear,   Our Lord, our God, died

called   on us,   And bid   us a - wake and pray.
on   the cross   For us   whom he loved so dear.

3 O fair, O fair Jerusalem,
    When shall I come to thee?
  When shall my sorrows have an end,
    Thy joy that I may see?

4 The fields were green as green could be,
    When from his glorious seat
  Our Lord, our God, he watered us,
    With his heavenly dew so sweet.

5 And for the saving of our souls
    Christ died upon the cross;
  We ne'er shall do for Jesus Christ
    As he hath done for us.

6 The life of man is but a span
    And cut down in its flower;
  We are here to-day, and to-morrow
    are gone,
  The creatures of an hour.

Tune noted by Miss Lucy Broadwood, in Surrey,
in 1894. Printed in the *Journal of the Folk Song Society*, vol. i, p. 176.

46 THE BELLMAN'S SONG
(GENERAL: THE PASSION)
THIRD TUNE

Traditional

Ibid.
(R.V.W.)

1. The_ moon shines bright, and the stars give a light: A
2. A - wake, a - wake, good_ peo - ple_ all; A -

lit - tle be-fore it was day   Our_ Lord, our_ God, he_
-wake, and_ you shall_ hear,   Our_ Lord, our_ God, died_

called_ on_ us, And bid us a - wake and pray.
on_ the_ cross For_ us whom he loved so dear.

3 O fair, O fair Jerusalem,
　　When shall I come to thee?
　When shall my sorrows have an end,
　　Thy joy that I may see?

4 The fields were green as green could be,
　　When from his glorious seat
　Our Lord, our God, he watered us,
　　With his heavenly dew so sweet.

5 And for the saving of our souls
　　Christ died upon the cross;
　We ne'er shall do for Jesus Christ
　　As he hath done for us.

6 The life of man is but a span
　　And cut down in its flower;
　We are here to-day, and to-morrow
　　are gone,
　　The creatures of an hour.

Tune noted at Kingsclere, Hants, by the late Godfrey Arkwright, in 1897, and printed in the
Journal of the Folk Song Society, vol. i, p. 178. Harmonies from the *English Hymnal*, where the tune
is called 'Newbury' and set to hymn 16.

47 MAY CAROL

Traditional

Ibid.
(R.V.W.)

VOICES IN UNISON

PIANO or ORGAN (all verses)

Slow

1. A - wake, a - wake, good peo - ple all, A-
-wake! and you shall_ hear That Christ has di - ed for_ our sins For he
lov - ed_ us so dear._____

1st time

Last time

2. So __
3.*The__
4. A __
5. Now my

pp

94

Melody (vv. 2-5)

2. So dear - ly, so dear - ly has Christ_ lov-ed us, And_
3. *The ear - ly_ cock so_ ear - - ly_ crows, That is

(v. 3)

for our_ sins was_ slain; Christ bids us leave off our_
pass - ing the night a - - way, For the trum - pet shall sound and the

wick - ed - ness And turn to the Lord a - - gain._
dead_ shall be raised, Lord, at the great judge - ment day. _

4. A branch of_may I have brought to_you, And at your door it stands; It

is but a sprout, but it's well_bud-ded out By the work of_our Lord's hands._

5. Now my song, that is done, and I_ must be gone, No lon-ger can I stay; So God

bless you all, both great_and small, And I wish you a joy-ful May._

For version for unaccompanied singing see overleaf.

VERSION FOR UNACCOMPANIED SINGING
(Sopranos should sing melody in vv. 2-5 as on page 97)

1. A - wake, a - wake, good peo - ple all, A - wake! and you shall

hear— That—Christ has di - ed— for— our sins For he lo - ved— us so— dear.

Copyright, 1919, by Stainer & Bell Ltd.

2 So dearly, so dearly has Christ lovèd us,
    And for our sins was slain;
  Christ bids us leave off our wickedness
    And turn to the Lord again.

3 *The early cock so early crows,
    That is passing the night away,
  For the trumpet shall sound and the dead shall be
      raised,
    Lord, at the great judgement day.

4 A branch of may I have brought to you,
    And at your door it stands;
  It is but a sprout, but it's well budded out
    By the work of our Lord's hands.

5 Now my song, that is done, and I must be gone,
    No longer can I stay;
  So God bless you all, both great and small,
    And I wish you a joyful May.

The melody and the text (exactly as here, except that 'was' has been put instead of 'were' in v. 2,
and 'but' added in v. 4) were taken from Mr. Flack, Fowlmere, Cambs., and printed in *Eight
Traditional English Carols* (Vaughan Williams), Stainer & Bell. Cecil Sharp and Miss Broadwood
have collected other versions. V. I is a variant of the second verse in the Bellman's Song, 'The
moon shines bright', No. 46. (See also *English County Songs*, and the *Journal of the Folk Song Society*,
i. 180.) The Worcestershire version collected by Sharp has the 'fields were green' verse of the
Bellman's Song.

2. So dear - ly, so dear - ly has Christ_ lov-ed us, And_
3. *The ear - ly_ cock so_ ear - - ly_ crows, That is

for our_ sins was_ slain; Christ bids us leave off our_
pass - ing the night a - - way, For the trum - pet shall sound and the

wick - ed - ness And turn to the Lord a - - gain._
dead_ shall be raised, Lord, at the great judge - ment day. _

4. A branch of_may I have brought to_ you, And at your door it stands; It_

is but a sprout, but it's well_bud-ded out By the work of_our Lord's hands._

5. Now my song, that is done, and I_ must be gone, No lon-ger can I stay; So God

bless you all, both great_and small, And I wish you a joy-ful May._

48 MAY-DAY GARLAND
(MAY)

Traditional

Ibid.
(M. S.)

1. I've brought you here a bunch of may! Be-fore your door it stands:— It's well set out, and well spread a-bout, By the work— of our Lord's hands:—— It's well set out,— and well spread a-bout, By the work— of our Lord's hands.——

2. This morn-ing is the first of May, The pri-mest of the year:— So la-dies all, both great— and small, I wish you— a joy-ful cheer:—— So la-dies all,— both great— and small, I— wish you a joy-ful cheer.——

3 Then take your bible in your hand,
  And read the scriptures through;
  And when the day of judgement comes,
  The Lord will remember you:
    And when the day, &c.

4 The clock's struck one! I must be gone!
  No longer can I stay.
  If I should live to carry again,
  I'll call another May:
    If I should live, &c.

This (or 46, or 47) might be sung in church at May-time, when Evensong is over, by one or two girls carrying a branch of may.
   The words and tune were taken by Geoffrey and Martin Shaw from an English girl (now Mrs. Betambeau), in the Boro' Polytechnic, London, c. 1917; she had brought them from Northamptonshire.
   A May carol from Hitchin is printed by Robert Bell in *Songs of the Peasantry*, 1857, of which verses 1 and 2 are the 1 and 2 of the Furry Day Carol; v. 3 is v. 4 of our May Carol and 1 of our Garland; and verses 4, 6, 7 are 4, 6 and 1 of the Bellman's Song.

49 FURRY DAY CAROL
(MAY)

Traditional

Ibid.
(M.S.)

1. Re-mem-ber_ us   poor_ May-ers_all! And_ thus we   do be-
2. *We have been ram-bling_ half   the_night, And_ al-most all_ the_

-gin - - a To lead our_ lives in __ right - eous - ness, Or_
day - - a, And   now, re - turn-ed__ back a - gain,   We've

sing_

else   we   die_ in sin - - a: *With Ho - lan - to,*
brought you a branch of__ may - - a: *With Ho - lan - to,*

mer - ry,_   O,   With_

Ho - lan - to,   Ho - lan - to,_ sing_ mer - - ry,   With

Ho - lan - to,

100

Ho - lan - to, sing＿ mer - ry,＿ O, With＿ Ho - lan - to,＿ sing＿ mer - ry!

3 O, we were up as soon as day,
  To fetch the summer home-a;
  The summer is a-coming on,
  And winter is a-gone-a:

  With Holan-to, etc.

4 Then let us all most merry be,
  And sing with cheerful voice-a;
  For we have good occasion now
  This time for to rejoice-a:

  With Holan-to, etc.

5 *Saint George he next shall be our song:
  Saint George, he was a knight-a;
  Of all the men in Christendom
  Saint George he was the right-a:

  With Holan-to, etc.

6 God bless our land with power and might,
  God send us peace in England;
  Pray send us peace both day and night,
  For ever in merry England:

  With Holan-to, etc.

This Furry Day Carol is distinct, both in words and tune, from the Furry Day Song, annually sung at the Spring festival in Helston in Cornwall (the tune of which is given by Gilbert), though there is some resemblance. We are indebted to Mr. Henry Jenner, F.S.A., for much kind information about the Helston festivities, and about the Furry Day Song, which includes references to Robin Hood and the Spaniards—doubtless of the Armada period. The tune of the Carol is given in Duncan's *Story of the Carol*, where he includes also a Robin Hood verse. (For the May verses cf. No. 48, n.). The tendency to confine carols to Christmas led to a Christmas version, which must be later. *Furry* is a corruption of the Latin *feria*, holiday (though in its ecclesiastical use it came to mean an unoccupied day and not a holy day). In Chaucer it is (through the Old French *feire, foire*) 'faire', and hence our 'village fair'.

50 NOS GALAN
(WINTER)

Pr. K.E. Roberts

Welsh
(M.S.)

SOPRANO
ALTO

1. Now the joy - ful bells a - ring - ing, *All___ ye_ moun - tains,*
2. Dear our home as dear none_ o - ther; *Where the_ moun - tains*
3. Cold the year, new white - ness_wear - ing, *All___ ye_ moun - tains,*

TENOR
BASS

praise the Lord! Lift our hearts, like_ birds a - wing - ing,
praise the Lord! Glad - ly here our_ care we _ smo - ther;
praise the Lord! Peace, good-will to ___ us a - bear - ing,

All___ ye_moun - tains, praise the Lord! Now our fes - tal
Where_ the_moun - tains praise the Lord! Here we know that
All ___ ye _ moun - tains, praise the Lord! Now we all God's

sea - son, bring-ing Kins - men_ all,_ to bide and_ board,
Christ our bro - ther Binds_ us_ all _ as by a _ cord:
good - ness shar-ing Break_ the_ bread_ and sheathe the_ sword:

102

Sets our chee - ry voi - ces_ sing-ing: *All__ ye_ moun-tains, praise the Lord!*
He was born of Ma - ry_ mo - ther *Where_ the_ moun-tains praise the Lord!*
Bright our hearths the sig - nal_ fla - ring, *All__ ye_ moun-tains, praise the Lord!*

Words based on the Welsh New Year's Eve secular Carol, Nos Galan.
On New Year's Eve or Day v. 3, l. 5 may be 'Now we all the New Year sharing'.

ALTERNATIVE WORDS

(*Secular*)

DECK the hall with boughs of holly,
  Fa la la la la la la la la,
'Tis the season to be jolly,
  Fa la, &c.
Fill the mead cup, drain the barrel,
  Fa la, &c.
Troll the ancient Christmas carol,
  Fa la, &c.

2 See the flowing bowl before us,
  Fa la la la la la la la la,
Strike the harp and join the chorus,
  Fa la, &c.
Follow me in merry measure,
  Fa la, &c.
While I sing of beauty's treasure,
  Fa la, &c.

3 Fast away the old year passes,
  Fa la la la la la la la la,
Hail the new, ye lads and lassies,
  Fa la, &c.
Laughing, quaffing, all together,
  Fa la, &c.
Heedless of the wind and weather,
  Fa la, &c.

Traditional

51 THE SINNERS' REDEMPTION
(GENERAL)

17th century

Traditional
(R.V.W.)

1. All you that are to mirth inclined, Consider well and bear in mind What our good God for us hath done, In sending his beloved Son.

2. Let all our songs and praises be Unto his heav'nly majesty; And evermore amongst our mirth, Remember Christ our Saviour's birth.

Copyright, 1919, by Stainer & Bell Ltd.

3 Moreover, let us every one
  Call unto mind and think upon
  His righteous life, and how he died,
  To have poor sinners justified.

4 He in the Temple daily taught,
  And many wonders strange he wrought.
  He gave the blind their perfect sight,
  And made the lame to walk upright.

5 He raisèd Lazarus from the grave,
  And to the sick their health he gave,
  But yet for all these wonders wrought,
  The priests his dire destruction sought:

6 With vile reproachful taunts and scorns
  They crowned him with a wreath of thorns:
  Then to the cross through hands and feet
  They nailed our blest Redeemer sweet;

7 Thus have you seen and heard aright,
  The love of Christ, the Lord of might;
  And how he shed his precious blood,
  Only to do us sinners good.

One of the most popular carols; some verses of it used to be reprinted annually on the broadsides. The tune was noted from Mr. Hall of Castleton, Derbyshire, with the first verse only. The late Rev. W. H. Shawcross published other verses in his *Old Castleton Christmas Carols*, but these are nearly identical with those in Husk, who notes the appearance of the carol on a music-sheet of 1775. Gilbert, 1822, prints a west-country version—some of the opening Christmas verses, but with a refrain and a different tune. Our tune is from *Eight Traditional Carols* (Vaughan Williams), Stainer & Bell. Cecil Sharp prints a different text and tune in his *English Folk-Carols*, VIII.

We have gone back to the earliest known original, and have selected from the twenty-eight verses in '*The Garland of Good-Will*, containing many Pleasant Songs and Poems—T——D—— London: Printed for *G. Conyers* at the Sign of the *Golden-Ring* in *Little-Britain*' (not dated, except in pencil, 'printed about 1699'). Thomas Deloney was a famous ballad-writer and poet of the people, and one of the earliest of story-writers in English (his works were published by the Clarendon Press, ed. F. O. Mann, 1912). He first published in 1583 and died *c.* 1600. The *Garland* was first published in 1593, but without our carol. To all editions of later date new poems, not by Deloney, were added (this among them, some time after 1631) down to 1709, or later.

52 ANGELUS AD VIRGINEM

(GENERAL, Medieval: ANNUNCIATION)

14th century

Ibid.
(John A. Parkinson)

For editorial notes see p. 108.

(3.) Ti - bi coe - le - sti nun - ti - o, Tan - ti se - cre - ti con - sci -
(4.) Tu - um ex - o - ra fi - li - um Ut se no - bis pro - pi - ti -

(3.) Ti - bi coe - le - sti nun - ti - o, Tan - ti se - cre - ti con - sci -
(4.) Tu - um ex - o - ra fi - li - um Ut se no - bis pro - pi - ti -

-o, Con - sen - ti - ens, Et cu - pi - ens Vi - de - re Fac - tum quod au - di -
-um Ex - hi - be - at, Et de - le - at Pec - ca - ta: Prae - stans aux - i - li -

-o, Con - sen - ti - ens, Et cu - pi - ens Vi - de - re Fac - tum quod au - di -
-um Ex - hi - be - at, Et de - le - at Pec - ca - ta: Prae - stans aux - i - li -

-o; Pa - ra - ta sum pa - re - re, De - i con - si - li - o'.
-um Vi - ta fru - i be - a - ta Post hoc ex - i - li - um.

-o; Pa - ra - ta sum pa - re - re, De - i con - si - li - o'.
-um Vi - ta fru - i be - a - ta Post hoc ex - i - li - um.

107

Sources: (a) B. M. Cotton Fragm. XXIX, c. 1250, a fragmentary two-part conductus setting, with the melody in the upper voice. (b) *The Dublin Troper* of c. 1360, now at Cambridge University Library, (Add. MS. 710) gives two differing three-part versions, with the melody in the middle voice. (c) B.M. Arundel 248, an early 14th-century MS., gives the melody only, but with Latin and English words. Facsimiles of (b) and (c) are given in Wooldridge's *Early English Harmony*, pl. 34, 46, 47. The three-part version given here is taken from (b) where the original pitch is a fifth lower for A.T.B.

Chaucer mentions this early carol, or rather sequence, in the *Milleres Tale*: Nicholas, the Clerk of Oxenford, sang it in the evening to the accompaniment of his 'gay sautrye',—

'On which he made a nightes melodye
So swetely, that al the chambre rong,
And *Angelus ad virginem* he song.'

We suggest that it is best sung in the original Latin, and even thus, one verse is here omitted. There is a modern rendering by Gabriel Gillett in *The English Carol Book* (Mowbray). The 14th-century translation in (c) is more difficult; here is the first verse:

'Gabriel from evene King, Sent to the maide swete, Broute hire blisful tiding, And faire he gan hire greten: Heil be thu ful of grace arith, For godes sone this evene lith For mannes loven Wile man becomen And taken Fles of the maiden brith, Maken fre for to maken Of sene and deules mith.'

Another Middle English version by the blind monk, John Audlay, is quoted by John Stevens in *Music and Poetry in the Early Tudor Court*, p. 40.

53 THE CARNAL AND THE CRANE
(GENERAL, Legendary)

Traditional

Ibid.
(R.V.W.)

1. As — I passed by a riv-er-side, And there as — I did rein, In — ar-gu-ment I — chanced to — hear A — car-nal and — a crane.
2. The — car-nal — said un-to the crane, 'If all the world should turn, Be-fore we had the — Fa - - ther, But — now we have — the Son.'

Copyright, 1920, by Stainer & Bell Ltd.

3 'From whence does the Son come?
    From where and from what place?'
He said: 'In a manger,
    Between an ox and ass.

4 'I pray thee,' said the carnal,
    'Tell me before thou go,
Was not the mother of Jesus
    Conceived by the Holy Ghost?'

5 'She was the purest virgin,
    And the cleanest from sin;
She was the handmaid of our Lord,
    And mother of our King.'

6 'Where is the golden cradle
    That Christ was rockèd in?
Where are the silken sheets
    That Jesus was wrapt in?'

7 'A manger was the cradle
    That Christ was rockèd in;
The provender the asses left,
    So sweetly he slept on.'

I. rein ('reign')—renne, run.
Cf. No. 54 and No. 55. The ballad of 'The Carnal and the Crane' (The Crow and the Crane) contains four subjects: (1) The conversation between the two birds; (2) The legend of Herod and the Cock (No. 54); (3) of The Lovely Lion (four verses); (4) of The Miraculous Harvest (No. 55). Imperfect versions of various portions have been taken down by Cecil Sharp, Miss Broadwood, and Vaughan Williams: these have been here collated with Sandys, and with Frank Sidgwick in *Popular Carols*. See F. C. Child's *Ballads*, ii, p. 7; and also *The Folk Song Society's Journal*, i. 183; iv. 22. *Carnal* seems to be from the French *corneille*, a crow, but *N.E.D.* leaves it with a query.
Melody and part of text from Mr. Hirons, Haven, Dilwyn, *Twelve Traditional Carols from Hereford-shire* (Leather and Vaughan Williams), Stainer & Bell.

54 KING HEROD AND THE COCK
(GENERAL, Legendary)

Traditional

Ibid.
(M.S.)

1. There was a star in__ Da-vid's land, So__ bright it did ap-pear In-to King He-rod's cham - ber, And__ bright-ly it__ shined there.

2. The wise men soon es-pied __ it, And__ told the king on high, A__ prince-ly babe was born that night No__ king could e'er__ de-stroy.

3 'If this be true,' King Herod said,
   'As thou hast told to me,
   This roasted cock that lies in the dish
   Shall crow full fences three.'

4 The cock soon thrustened and feathered well,
   By the work of God's own hand,
   And he did crow full fences three,
   In the dish where he did stand.

Alternative to Verse 3

S. A. T.
sing 'Ah'

3. 'If this be true,' King He - rod said, 'As

thou hast told to me, This_ roast - ed cock that

lies in the dish Shall crow full fen - ces three.'

3. fences or 'sences'—times. 4. thrustened—(Early Mid. Eng.), pressed, thrust out.
Cf. No. 53 and No. 55. Words and tune from Mrs. Plumb, Armscote, Worcestershire (*Cecil Sharp*;
by permission of Novello & Co., Ltd.). The cock story is also in a ballad of St. Stephen, and is told of
others: it has been traced to *c.* 1200 in Prior's *Ancient Danish Ballads*.

55 THE MIRACULOUS HARVEST

(GENERAL, Legendary)

Traditional

Ibid.
(R. V. W.)

1. 'Rise up, rise up, you merry men all, See that you ready be: All children under two years old Now slain they all shall be.'

2. Then Jesus, aye, and Joseph, And Mary that was unknown, They travelled by a husbandman, Just while his seed was sown.

3 'God speed your work,' said Jesus,
'Throw all your seed away,
And carry home as ripened corn
What you have sown this day;

4 'For to keep your wife and family
From sorrow, grief, and pain,
And keep Christ in remembrance
Till seed-time comes again.'

5 The husbandman fell on his knees,
  Even upon his face;
  'Long time hast thou been lookèd for,
  But now thou'rt come at last.

6 *'And I myself do now believe
  Thy name is Jesus called;
  Redeemer of mankind thou art,
  Though undeserving all.'

7 After that there came King Herod,

  With his train so furiously,
  Enquiring of the husbandman

  Whether Jesus had passed by.

8 'Why, the truth it must be spoke,

  And the truth it must be known,
  For Jesus he passed by this way,
  Just as my seed was sown.

9 'But now I have it reapen,
  And some laid in my wain,
  Ready to fetch and carry
  Into my barn again.'

10 *'Turn back,' then says the Captain,
  'Your labour and mine's in vain;
  It's full three quarters of a year
  Since he his seed has sown.'

11 *So Herod was deceivèd

  By the work of God's own hand:
  No further he proceeded
  Into the Holy Land.

12 There's thousands of children young,
  Which for his sake did die;
  Do not forbid those little ones,
  And do not them deny.

The tune here set to *The Miraculous Harvest* was noted by Miss Lucy Broadwood from some gypsies of the name of Goby in 1893. They sang it to the following words, which are an interesting example of the way old ballads become confused among illiterate singers. The illiterate, however, often preserve in their own way what the educated lose: King Pharim (Pharaoh), for instance, may go back to the apocryphal *Gospel of the Infancy* (the Holy Family 'went down to Memphis, and having seen Pharaoh, they stayed three years in Egypt, and the Lord Jesus wrought many miracles there'). These apocryphal legends seem to have got into ballads through the preaching Friars. See Miss Broadwood's *English Traditional Songs and Carols* (Boosey), and *Journal of the Folk Song Society* (1910), iv. 24, for further information.

  King Pharim: 1. King Pharim sat a-musing, A-musing all alone; There came a blessed Saviour, And all to him unknown. 2. 'Say, where did you come from, good man, O where did you then pass?' 'It is out of the land Egypt, Between an ox and ass.' 3. 'O, if you come out of Egypt, man, One thing I fain I known, Whether a blessed Virgin Mary Sprung from an Holy Ghost?' 4. For if this is true, is true, good man, That you've been telling to me, That the roasted cock do crow three times In the place where they did stand.' 5. O, it's straight away the cock did fetch, And feathered to your own hand, Three times a roasted cock did crow, On the place where they did stand. 6. Joseph, Jesus and Mary Were travelling for the West, When Mary grew a-tired She might sit down and rest. 7. They travelled further and further, The weather being so warm, Till they came unto some husbandman A-sowing of his corn. 8. 'Come, husbandman,' cried Jesus, 'From over speed and pride, And carry home your ripened corn That you've been sowing this day. 9. For to keep your wife and family From sorrow, grief and pain, And keep Christ in your remembrance Till the time comes round again.'

  In the *English Hymnal* and *Songs of Praise* the tune is named 'Capel'.

56 THE HOLY WELL
(GENERAL, Legendary)
FIRST TUNE

Traditional

Ibid.
(E.M.)

1. As it fell out one May morn-ing, And up-on a bright ho-li-day, Sweet Je-sus asked of his dear mo-ther If he might go to play. 'To play, to play, sweet Je-sus shall go, And to play now get you gone; And

2. Sweet Je-sus went down to yon-der town, As far as the Ho-ly Well, And there did see as fine chil-dren As a-ny tongue can tell. He said, 'God bless you ev-'ry one, And your bodies Christ save and see! And

let   me hear of no com-plaint At night when you come home.'
now, lit-tle chil-dren, I'll play with you, And you shall play with me.'

3 But they made answer to him, 'No!
   Thou art meaner than us all;

  Thou art but a simple fair maid's child,
   Born in an ox's stall.'
  Sweet Jesus turned him round about,
   Neither laughed, nor smiled, nor spoke;

  But the tears came trickling from his eyes
   Like waters from the rock.

4 Sweet Jesus turned him round about,
   To his mother's dear home went he,

  And said, 'I have been in yonder town,
   As after you may see:
  I have been down in yonder town,

  As far as the Holy Well;

  There did I meet with as fine children
   As any tongue can tell.

5 'I said, "God bless you every one,
   And your bodies Christ save and see!

  And now, little children, I'll play with you,
   And you shall play with me."
  But they made answer to me, "No";
   They were lords' and ladies' sons,
  And I the meanest of them all,
   Born in an ox's stall.'

6 'Though you are but a maiden's child,
   Born in an ox's stall,
  Thou art the Christ, the King of heaven,

  And the Saviour of them all!

  Sweet Jesus, go down to yonder town,

  As far as the Holy Well,
  And take away those sinful souls,
   And dip them deep in hell.'

7 'Nay, nay,' sweet Jesus smiled and said;
   'Nay, nay, that may not be,
  For there are too many sinful souls

  Crying out for the help of me.'

  Then up spoke the angel Gabriel,
   Upon a good set steven,

  'Although you are but a maiden's child,
   You are the King of heaven!'

3. simple—orig. 'silly': see note to No. 2. 7. steven—voice, an Anglo-Saxon word; it occurs in Spenser and still survives in dialect. Sometimes corrupted to 'our good Saint Stephen'.
   Two Herefordshire versions collated with Sandys, 1833, and with the fine version printed by Frank Sidgwick. Melody from Sandys.

56 THE HOLY WELL
(GENERAL, Legendary)

SECOND TUNE

Traditional

Ibid.
(R.V.W.)

1. As it fell out one May morn-ing, And up-
'To play, to play, sweet Je-sus shall go, And to

-on a bright ho-li-day, Sweet Je-sus asked of his
play now get you gone; And let me hear of

dear mo-ther If he might go to
no com-plaint At night when you come

play, if he might go to play.
home, at night when you come home.'

2 Sweet Jesus went down to yonder town,

As far as the Holy Well,
And there did see as fine children
As any tongue can tell.
He said, 'God bless you every one,

And your bodies Christ save and see!

And now, little children, I'll play with you,
And you shall play with me.'

3 But they made answer to him, 'No!
Thou art meaner than us all;

Thou art but a simple fair maid's child,
Born in an ox's stall.'
Sweet Jesus turned him round about,
Neither laughed, nor smiled, nor spoke;

But the tears came trickling from his eyes
Like waters from the rock.

4 Sweet Jesus turned him round about,

To his mother's dear home went he,

And said, 'I have been in yonder town,
As after you may see:
I have been down in yonder town,

As far as the Holy Well;
There did I meet with as fine children
As any tongue can tell.

5 'I said, "God bless you every one,

And your bodies Christ save and see!

And now, little children, I'll play with you,
And you shall play with me."
But they made answer to me, "No";
They were lords' and ladies' sons,
And I the meanest of them all,
Born in an ox's stall.'

6 'Though you are but a maiden's child,
Born in an ox's stall,
Thou art the Christ, the King of heaven,

And the Saviour of them all!
Sweet Jesus, go down to yonder town,

As far as the Holy Well,
And take away those sinful souls,
And dip them deep in hell.'

7 'Nay, nay,' sweet Jesus smiled and said;
'Nay, nay, that may not be,
For there are too many sinful souls
Crying out for the help of me.'

Then up spoke the angel Gabriel,
Upon a good set steven,
'Although you are but a maiden's child,
You are the King of heaven!'

3. simple—orig. 'silly': see note to No. 2. 7. steven—voice, an Anglo-Saxon word; it occurs in Spenser and still survives in dialect. Sometimes corrupted to 'our good Saint Stephen'.

Tune noted by Cecil Sharp, at Camborne, 1913.
Printed in the *Journal of the Folk Song Society*, vol. v, p. 4.

57 DIVES AND LAZARUS
(GENERAL)

FIRST TUNE

Traditional

Ibid.
(R.V.W.)

SOPRANO
ALTO

TENOR
BASS

1. As＿ it fell＿ out up - on one day, Rich＿
2. Then La - za-rus laid him＿ down and down, And＿

Di - ves made a＿ feast, And he in - vi - ted＿
down at Di - ves'＿ door: 'Some meat and drink, bro-ther

all his friends And＿ gen - try of the best.
Di - ve - rus, Be - stow up - on the poor.'

3 'Thou'rt none of my brothers, Lazarus,
　That liest begging at my door;
No meat, nor drink will I give thee,
　Nor bestow upon the poor.'

4 *Then Lazarus laid him down and down,
　All under Dives' wall:
'Some meat, some drink, brother Diverus,
　For hunger starve I shall.'

5 *'Thou'rt none of my brothers, Lazarus,
　That liest begging at my wall;
No meat, nor drink will I give thee,
　For hunger starve you shall.'

6 *Then Lazarus laid him down and down,
　And down at Dives' gate:
'Some meat! some drink! brother Diverus,
　For Jesus Christ his sake.'

7 *'Thou'rt none of my brothers, Lazarus,
 That liest begging at my gate;
No meat, no drink will I give thee,
 For Jesus Christ his sake.'

8 *Then Dives sent out his hungry dogs,
 To bite him as he lay;
They hadn't the power to bite one bite,
 But licked his sores away.

9 *Then Dives sent to his merry men,
 To worry poor Lazarus away;
They'd not the power to strike one stroke,
 But flung their whips away.

10 As it fell out upon one day,
 Poor Lazarus sickened and died;
There came two angels out of heaven,
 His soul therein to guide.

11 'Rise up! rise up! brother Lazarus,
 And go along with me;
For you've a place prepared in heaven,
 To sit on an angel's knee.'

12 As it fell out upon one day,
 Rich Dives sickened and died;
There came two serpents out of hell,
 His soul therein to guide.

13 'Rise up! rise up! brother Diverus,
 And come along with me;
There is a place provided in hell
 For wicked men like thee.'

14 *Then Dives looked up with his eyes
 And saw poor Lazarus blest;

'Give me one drop of water, brother Lazarus,
To quench my flaming thirst.

15 *'O, was I now but alive again
 The space of one half hour!
O, that I had my peace again
 Then the devil should have no power!'

V. 13, 1. 4. In some versions 'To sit upon a serpent's knee', which is generally preferred by choirs.
The text is the result of a collation of the two Herefordshire texts mentioned below with the help
of other versions. A version of eighteen verses is given by Mr. F. Sidgwick in his *Popular Carols*. The
various recurring words (such as 'Dives' (Divus), 'upon one day', &c.) have been made to conform
with the version associated with the melody. The following verses are taken entirely from the other
versions—2, 3, 11, 12, 13, 14, 15.
 Melody from Mr. John Evans, Dilwyn. Text from Mr. John Evans and Mrs. Harris, Eardisley, &c.
From *Twelve Traditional Carols from Herefordshire* (Leather and Vaughan Williams), Stainer & Bell.
 The Elizabethan dramatist, Fletcher, mentions 'the merry ballad of Dives and Lazarus' in his
Monsieur Thomas. Sylvester in 1861 claims to be the first to include it in a collection, giving it (but
he was not a scrupulous transcriber) from an old Birmingham broadside. Hone includes it in his
list, 1822; and Husk prints it from an eighteenth-century Worcester sheet. See also F. C. Child's
Ballads, ii, p. 10.
 This carol may be sung to the second tune of No. 60.

57 DIVES AND LAZARUS
(GENERAL)

SECOND TUNE

Traditional

Ibid.
(R.V.W.)

3 'Thou'rt none of my brothers, Lazarus,
   That liest begging at my door;
   No meat, nor drink will I give thee,
   Nor bestow upon the poor.'

4 *Then Lazarus laid him down and down,
   All under Dives' wall:
   'Some meat, some drink, brother Diverus,
   For hunger starve I shall.'

5 *'Thou'rt none of my brothers, Lazarus,
   That liest begging at my wall;
   No meat, nor drink will I give thee,
   For hunger starve you shall.'

6 *Then Lazarus laid him down and down,
   And down at Dives' gate:
   'Some meat! some drink! brother Diverus,
   For Jesus Christ his sake.'

7 *'Thou'rt none of my brothers, Lazarus,
  That liest begging at my gate;
No meat, no drink will I give thee,
  For Jesus Christ his sake.'

8 *Then Dives sent out his hungry dogs,
  To bite him as he lay;
They hadn't the power to bite one bite,
  But licked his sores away.

9 *Then Dives sent to his merry men,
  To worry poor Lazarus away;
They'd not the power to strike one stroke,
  But flung their whips away.

10 As it fell out upon one day,
  Poor Lazarus sickened and died;
There came two angels out of heaven,
  His soul therein to guide.

11 'Rise up! rise up! brother Lazarus,
  And go along with me;
For you've a place prepared in heaven,
  To sit on an angel's knee.'

12 As it fell out upon one day,
  Rich Dives sickened and died;
There came two serpents out of hell,
  His soul therein to guide.

13 'Rise up! rise up! brother Diverus,
  And come along with me;
There is a place provided in hell
  For wicked men like thee.'

14 *Then Dives looked up with his eyes
  And saw poor Lazarus blest;

♩ |♫ ♫ ♫ ♫

'Give me one drop of water, brother Lazarus,
  To quench my flaming thirst.

♫

15 *'O, was I now but alive again
  The space of one half hour!
O, that I had my peace again
  Then the devil should have no power!'

Tune noted for Mrs. Leather at Eardisley, Herefordshire, by Miss Andrews and Dr. Darling, in 1905. Harmonies from the *English Hymnal*, where the tune is called 'Eardisley', and is set to hymn 601. Also *Songs of Praise* No. 393.
  This carol may be sung to the second tune of No. 60.

58 JACOB'S LADDER
(GENERAL)

Traditional

Ibid.
(M.S.)

SOPRANO
ALTO

TENOR
BASS

SEMI-CHORUS

1. As Ja - cob with tra - vel was wea - ry one day, At
2. This lad - der is long, it is strong and well-made, Has stood

night on a stone for a pil - low he lay; He saw in a
hun - dreds of years and is not yet de - cayed; Ma - ny mil - lions have

vi - sion a lad - der so high, That its foot was on
climbed it and reached Si - on's hill, And thou - sands by

FULL

earth and its top in the sky: *Al - le - lu - ya to Je - sus, who*
faith are climb - ing it still: *faith are climb - ing it still:*

122

died on the tree,— And hath raised up a lad - der of mer - cy for

me, And hath raised up a lad - der of mer - cy for me.

3 Come, let us ascend! all may climb it who will;
   For the angels of Jacob are guarding it still:
   And remember, each step that by faith we pass o'er,
   Some prophet or martyr hath trod it before:

   Alleluya etc.

4 And when we arrive at the haven of rest,
   We shall hear the glad words, 'Come up hither, ye blest,
   Here are regions of light, here are mansions of bliss.'
   O, who would not climb such a ladder as this?

   Alleluya etc.

This is apparently a carol to which new words were fitted under the influence of the Methodist revival. It is printed here with its traditional melody, which Stainer made familiar in 1871.

59 WELSH CAROL
(GENERAL: WHITSUNTIDE)

Pr. K.E. Roberts

Welsh
(Dr. Caradog Roberts)

1. A - wake were they on - ly, those shep-herds so lone-ly, On guard in that si - lence pro - found:___ When co - lour had fa - ded, when night-time had sha - ded Their sen - ses from sight and from sound, Lo,___ then broke a won-der, then drif - ted a - sun-der The veils from the splen-dour of

2. May light now en - fold us, O Lord, for be - hold us Like shep-herds, from tu - mult with - drawn,___ Nor hear - ing, nor see - ing, all oth - er care flee - ing, We wait the in - eff - a - ble dawn. O___ Spi - rit all- know-ing, thou source o - ver - flow-ing, O move in the dark-ness a-

By permission of the Caniedydd Committee, Welsh Congregational Union.

A paraphrase of the Welsh Carol, 'Roedd yn y wlad honno'.

60 JOB
(GENERAL)
FIRST TUNE

Traditional

Ibid.
(M.S.)

1. Come all you wor - thy Christ - ian men That dwell up - on this land, Don't spend your time in ri - ot - ing; Re - mem - ber you're but man. Be watch - ful for your lat - ter end; Be

2. Now, Job he was a pa - tient man, The rich - est in the East: When he was brought to pov - er - ty, His sor - rows soon in - creased. He bore them all most pa - tient - ly; From

rea - dy for your— call. There are ma - ny chan - ges—
sin he did re - frain; He — al - ways trust - ed—

in this world;— Some— rise— while— oth - ers fall.
in the Lord;— He — soon— got — rich— a - gain.

3 Come all you worthy Christian men
  That are so very poor,
  Remember how poor Lazarus
  Lay at the rich man's door,
  While begging of the crumbs of bread
  That from his table fell.
  The scriptures do inform us all
  That in heaven he doth dwell.

4 The time, alas, it soon will come
  When parted we shall be;
  But all the difference it will make
  Is in joy and misery;
  And we must give a strict account
  Of great as well as small.
  Believe me, now, dear Christian friends,
  That God will judge us all.

Tune taken by Cecil Sharp from Mrs. Woodberry, Ash Priors,
Somerset, *Folk Songs from Somerset*, No. 88 (by permission of Novello & Co. Ltd.).

60 JOB
(GENERAL)
SECOND TUNE

Traditional

Ibid.
(M.S.)

1. Come all you wor-thy Christ-ian men That dwell up-on this land, Don't spend your time in ri-ot-ing; Re-mem-ber you're but man. Be watch-ful for your lat-ter end; Be rea-dy for your

2. Now, Job he was a pa-tient man, The rich-est in the East: When he was brought to pov-er-ty, His sor-rows soon in-creased. He bore them all most pa-tient-ly; From sin he did re-

call._____ There are ma - ny chan - ges__ in this world; Some_
-frain; _____ He __ al - ways trust - ed __ in the Lord; He__

1st time   *Last time*

rise while oth - ers fall._____ Be __ fall.
soon got rich _ a - gain._____ He__ -gain._____

3 Come all you worthy Christian men
  That are so very poor,
  Remember how poor Lazarus
  Lay at the rich man's door,
  While begging of the crumbs of bread
  That from his table fell.
  The scriptures do inform us all
  That in heaven he doth dwell.

4 The time, alas, it soon will come
  When parted we shall be;
  But all the difference it will make
  Is in joy and misery;
  And we must give a strict account
  Of great as well as small.
  Believe me, now, dear Christian friends,
  That God will judge us all.

Tune noted by the late A. J. Hipkins in Westminster and printed in *English County Songs* to the words of 'Dives and Lazarus', but it probably belongs to 'Job'. It belongs more properly, however, to the above words. (Cf. the hymn-tune 'Kingsfold', E.H. 574).

60 JOB
(GENERAL)
THIRD TUNE

Traditional

Ibid.
(R.V.W.)

1. Come all you wor-thy Christ-ian men_ That_ dwell up-on_ this_ land,_ Don't spend your time in_ ri - ot-ing; Re - mem-ber you're but man.___ Be watch-ful for your lat - ter end; Be

2. Now, Job he was a pa-tient man,_ The_ rich - est in_ the_ East:_ When he was brought to pov-er-ty, His_ sor-rows soon_ in - creased.___ He bore them all most pa-tient-ly; From

130

rea - dy for your — call. _____ There are ma — ny chan - ges
sin he did re - frain; _____ He _____ al - ways trust - ed

in this world; Some _ rise while oth - ers_ fall.
in the Lord; He _ soon got rich_ a - - gain.

By permission of Novello & Co.

3 Come all you worthy Christian men
That are so very poor,
Remember how poor Lazarus
Lay at the rich man's door,
While begging of the crumbs of bread
That from his table fell.
The scriptures do inform us all
That in heaven he doth dwell.

4 The time, alas, it soon will come
When parted we shall be;
But all the difference it will make
Is in joy and misery;
And we must give a strict account
Of great as well as small.
Believe me, now, dear Christian friends,
That God will judge us all.

Tune noted by W. Percy Merrick and printed in the *Journal of the Folk Song Society*, vol. i, p. 74. Also published as a solo song in *Folk Songs from Sussex* (Novello).

60 JOB
(GENERAL)
FOURTH TUNE

Traditional

Ibid.
(R. V. W.)

1. Come all you wor - thy Christ - ian men That dwell up - on this land, Don't spend your time in ri - ot - ing; Re - mem - ber you're but man. Be watch - ful for your lat - ter end; Be

2. Now, Job he was a pa - tient man, The rich - est in the East: When he was brought to pov - er - ty, His sor - rows soon in - creased. He bore them all most pa - tient - ly; From

132

3 Come all you worthy Christian men
  That are so very poor,
  Remember how poor Lazarus
  Lay at the rich man's door,
  While begging of the crumbs of bread
  That from his table fell.
  The scriptures do inform us all
  That in heaven he doth dwell.

4 The time, alas, it soon will come
  When parted we shall be;
  But all the difference it will make
  Is in joy and misery;
  And we must give a strict account
  Of great as well as small.
  Believe me, now, dear Christian friends,
  That God will judge us all.

Tune noted by R. Vaughan Williams, near Horsham,
in 1904, and printed in the *Journal of the Folk Song Society*, vol. ii, p. 118.

61 DOWN IN YON FOREST
(GENERAL)

Traditional

Ibid.
(R.V.W.)

Copyright, 1919, by Stainer & Bell Ltd.

NOTE. It is suggested that the solo portion be sung without harmony in the opening verses; also that the solo portion be divided among various voices (male and female).

3 At the bed-side there lies a stone:
　Which the sweet Virgin Mary knelt upon:

4 Under that bed there runs a flood:
　The one half runs water, the other runs blood:

5 At the bed's foot there grows a thorn:
　Which ever blows blossom since he was born:

6 *Over that bed the moon shines bright:
　Denoting our Saviour was born this night:

Melody and text taken from Mr. Hall, Castleton, Derbyshire, by R. Vaughan Williams (*Eight Traditional Carols*), Stainer & Bell. Text unaltered except for (4) *flood* for 'river', (5) *bed's foot* for 'foot of the bed'.
　Cf. another folk version in No. 184. The earliest version is one only found in Richard Hill's MS. (cf. No. 36), and is printed below; it is in a different metre, but the hall, the bed, the knight of No. 184, the maid, and the stone are all there, and the words 'Corpus Christi' are written on the stone; the mystical meaning of the fifteenth-century original was therefore eucharistic, the altar and the sacrifice, while the thorn (not in the Hill MS.) and other allusions of this and the other two versions point to an interweaving of the legend of the Holy Grail. See F. Sidgwick, *Notes and Queries* (1905), iv. 181; *Folk Song Soc. J.* (1910), iv. 52; Greene, No. 322.
　The text of the carol in the Hill MS. (c. 1500), printed by Dyboski and others is: *Lully, lulley, lully, lulley! The falcon hath borne my make away.* 1. He bare him up, he bare him down, He bare him in to an orchard brown [*Refrain*]. 2. In that orchard there was an hall, That was hanged with purple and pall. 3. And in that hall there was a bed, It was hanged with gold so red. 4. And in that bed there lieth a knight, His wounds bleeding day and night. 5. By that bed's side kneeleth a may, And she weepeth both night and day. 6. And by that bed's side there standeth a stone, 'Corpus Christi' written thereon.

62 ALL AND SOME
(GENERAL, Medieval)

c. 1450

Ibid.
(M.S.)

No - well sing we, both all— and some, Now Rex pa - ci - fi - cus

is y - come. 1. Ex - or - -tum est in love and lysse. Now
2. De fruc-tu ven-tris of Ma - ry bright, Both

Christ his gree he gan— us gysse, And with his bo - dy us
God and man in her— a - light, Out of di - sease— he

brought to bliss, *Both all— and some, both all and some.*
did us dight:

The burden should be sung again after the last verse.

3 *Puer natus* to us was sent,
To bliss us bought, fro bale us blent,
And else to woe we had ywent:

4 *Lux fulgebit* with love and light,
In Mary mild his pennon pight,
In her took kind with manly might:

5 *Gloria tibi*, ay, and bliss,
God unto his grace he us wysse,
The rent of heaven that we not miss:

1. *Exortum est*—it is risen up. lysse—comfort, joy. gree (in MS. 'gre he')—favour. gysse—to prepare, attire (= guise). 2. *De fructu*, &c.—of the fruit of the womb. disease ('dysese')—dis-ease, discomfort, misery. dight—orig. dictate; prepare, hence make ready, array (revived by Walter Scott in the last sense). 3. *Puer natus*—a boy born. fro—from. bale—sorrow. blent—blenched, turned aside. ywent—gone. 4. *Lux*, &c.—the light will shine. pight—pitched. kind—nature. 5. *Gloria tibi*—glory to thee. wysse—guide. rent—tenure.
Source: Bodleian Library, Selden MS. b. 26, c. 1450, printed with transcription, in Stainer's *Early Bodleian Music*, and, more accurately, in *Medieval Carols*, No. 16 (Greene, No. 29). In the version above, spelling and harmony have been modernized.

135

63 GREEN GROW'TH THE HOLLY
(GENERAL)

O.B.C. version

16th century
(M.T.)

SOPRANO

1. Green grow'th the hol - ly, So doth the
2. Gay are the flow - ers, Hedge - rows and

ALTO

1. Green grow'th the hol - ly, So doth the
2. Gay are the flow - ers, Hedge - rows and

TENOR

1. Green grow'th the hol - ly, ____ So doth the
2. Gay are the flow - ers, ____ Hedge-rows and

i - vy; Though win - ter blasts blow ne'er ____ so
plough-lands; The days grow long - er in ____ the

i - vy; Though win - ter blasts blow ne'er ____ so
plough-lands; The days grow long - er in ____ the

i - vy; Though win - ter blasts blow ne'er ____ so
plough-lands; The days grow long - er in ____ the

high, Green grow'th the hol - ly.
sun, Soft fall the show - ers.

high, Green grow'th the hol - ly.
sun, Soft fall the show - ers.

high, Green grow'th ____ the hol - ly.
sun, Soft fall ____ the show - ers.

3 Full gold the harvest,
  Grain for thy labour;
     With God must work for daily bread,
  Else, man, thou starvest.

4 Fast fall the shed leaves,
  Russet and yellow;
     But resting-buds are snug and safe
  Where swung the dead leaves.

5 Green grow'th the holly,
  So doth the ivy;
     The God of life can never die.
  Hope! saith the holly.

The music, one of the songs in B.M. Add. MS. 31922 (c. 1515) attributed to Henry VIII, has survived in this refrain, 'Green grow'th the holly', &c. (attached to a love-song in a different metre and with no tune extant); it has been transcribed by Lady Mary Trefusis, and other verses have been added in the metre of the old melody. The original version is given in Musica Britannica, vol. xviii.

64 A NEW DIAL
(GENERAL)

1625

Traditional
(M.S.)

In those twelve days let us be glad, in those twelve days let
us be glad, For God of his power hath all things made.

1. What are they that are but one? What are they that
2. What are they that are but two? What are they that

are but one? One God, one Bap - tism, and one
are but two? Two Tes - ta - ments, the old and

Faith, One Truth there is, the scrip - ture saith:
new, We do ac - know - ledge to be true:

3 What are they that are but three?
  Three Persons are in Trinity
  Which make one God in unity:

4 What are they that are but four?
  Four sweet Evangelists there are,
  Christ's birth, life, death, which do declare:

5 *What are they that are but five?
  Five Senses, like five kings, maintain
  In every man a several reign:

6 *What are they that are but six?
  Six Days to labour is not wrong,
  For God himself did work so long:

7 *What are they that are but seven?
  Seven Liberal Arts hath God sent down
  With divine skill man's soul to crown:

8 *What are they that are but eight?
  Eight Beatitudes are there given;
  Use them aright and go to heaven:

9 *What are they that are but nine?
  Nine Muses, like the heavens' nine spheres,
  With sacred tunes entice our ears:

10 *What are they that are but ten?
  Ten Statutes God to Moses gave,
  Which, kept or broke, do spill or save:

11 *What are they that are but eleven?
  Eleven thousand Virgins did partake,
  And suffered death for Jesus' sake:

12 *What are they that are but twelve?
  Twelve are attending on God's Son;
  Twelve make our Creed. The dial's done:

In an almanack of 1625, in the Bagford collection. Gilbert (1822) prints a version too rough to be sung without constant mispronunciation and alteration of the music; this version is smoothed by Sandys, but is still almost unsingable. The refrain (from Gilbert) is not given in the almanack, but was probably then known. This 1625 version is evidently by a scholar working on a much older carol; and it is curious to see how the scholarly parts are absent from the folk-version of 1822. Two verses (and the tune) are from Sandys: v. 8 (Gilbert's singer gave 'Altitudes' instead of 'Beatitudes') where the Almanack has, 'Eight in Noah's Ark alive were found, When (in a word) the World lay drown'd'; and v. 11 (the same, but more confused, in Gilbert), where the Almanack rejects the Virgins of Cologne, only to give a duplicate Apostle verse, 'Eleven with Christ in Heaven do dwell, The Twelfth for ever burns in Hell'.

The Seven Liberal Arts (changed in Gilbert to 'Seven Days in week') and the Eleven Thousand Virgins point to a medieval origin for both verses. V. 5, We now know that there are more than five senses. V. 7, The Seven Liberal arts (the *Trivium* and *Quadrivium* of thirteenth-century schoolmen, and of St. Augustine, Boethius, and Cassiodorus) were: grammar, rhetoric, and dialectic, arithmetic, geometry, astronomy, and music. V. 9, The Nine Muses of the Greeks were: Calliope (epic song), Clio (history), Euterpe (lyric song), Thalia (comedy), Melpomene (tragedy), Terpsichore (dancing), Erato (erotic poetry), Polymnia (sacred songs), Urania (astronomy). V. 11, There are various explanations of the extravagant legend of St. Ursula and the Eleven Thousand Virgins (familiar through the paintings of Memlinc and Carpaccio): one is that it originated in an inscription to 'Ursula et Undecimilla, virgines', another that there were originally Ursula and eleven Martyrs, the MM. being read as 'thousand'. V. 12, The Twelve Apostles, and the twelve articles of the Apostles' Creed: each article is sometimes represented in art on a scroll held by an Apostle.

65 THE DECREE
(GENERAL)

FIRST TUNE

Traditional

Ibid.
(M.S.)

1. Let Christ-ians all with one ac-cord re-joice, And prai-ses
2. What pains and la-bours did not Christ en-dure To save our

sing, with heart as well as voice, To God on high, for glo-rious things he's
souls and hap-pi-ness se-cure! Was al-ways do-ing good, to let us

done, In send-ing us ___ his best-be-lov-ed Son.
see By his ex-am-ple what we ought to be.

FA-BURDEN (melody in the bass)

to see,

3. He made the blind to see, the lame to go, He raised the

140

dead, which none but he could do: He cured the lepers of infected

e - vils, And by his mighty power he cast out devils.

4 But yet for all the wonders that he wrought,
   Ungrateful men still his destruction sought:
   Then to a cross the Saviour of mankind
   Was led, an harmless Lamb, as was designed.

5 Thus blessèd Jesus freely did resign
   His precious soul to save both thine and mine;
   Then let us all his mercies highly prize,
   Who for our sins was made a sacrifice.

Selected verses from the long carol of twenty-three, which takes its name 'The Black Decree'
from three verses about the massacre of the Innocents, in the Dudley collection, A Good Christmas
Box, 1847, which preserved the words. The verses were evidently written by one author, and
not earlier than the eighteenth century, perhaps to replace some older folk-carol which had been
associated with the tune. Stainer restored the second traditional melody; the first melody, also
proper to the words, was noted by Cecil Sharp in an unpublished MS.

65 THE DECREE
(GENERAL)
SECOND TUNE

Traditional

Ibid.
(M.S.)

1. Let Christ-ians all with one ac - cord re - joice, And prai - ses sing, with heart as well as voice, To God on high, for glo-rious things he's done, In send-ing us his best-be - lov - ed Son.

2. What pains and la - bours did not Christ en - dure To save our souls and hap-pi - ness se - cure! Was al-ways do - ing good, to let us see By his ex - am - ple what we ought to be.

3 He made the blind to see, the lame to go,
He raised the dead, which none but he could do:

He cured the lepers of infected evils,

And by his mighty power he cast out devils.

4 But yet for all the wonders that he wrought,
Ungrateful men still his destruction sought:
Then to a cross the Saviour of mankind
Was led, an harmless Lamb, as was designed.

5 Thus blessèd Jesus freely did resign
His precious soul to save both thine and mine;
Then let us all his mercies highly prize,
Who for our sins was made a sacrifice.

See footnote to first tune.

142

66 THE CHERRY TREE CAROL

PART 1 (GENERAL, Legendary)

FIRST TUNE

Traditional

Ibid.
(M.S.)

1. Jo-seph was an old man, And an old man was he,
2. Jo-seph and Ma-ry Walked through an or-chard good,

Verses [6, 9, 10]

When he wed-ded Ma-ry In the land of Ga-li-lee.
Where was cher-ries and ber-ries So red as an-y blood.

3 *Joseph and Mary
    Walked through an orchard green,
  Where was berries and cherries
    As thick as might be seen.

4 O then bespoke Mary,
    With words so meek and mild,
  'Pluck me one cherry, Joseph,
    For I am with child.'

5 *O then bespoke Joseph,
    With answer most unkind,
  'Let him pluck thee a cherry
    That brought thee now with child.'

6 *O then bespoke the baby
    Within his mother's womb—
  'Bow down then the tallest tree
    For my mother to have some.'

7 Then bowed down the highest tree,
    Unto his mother's hand.
  Then she cried, 'See, Joseph,
    I have cherries at command.'

8 *O then bespoke Joseph—
    'I have done Mary wrong;
  But now cheer up, my dearest,
    And do not be cast down.

9 'O eat your cherries, Mary,
    O eat your cherries now,
  O eat your cherries, Mary,
    That grow upon the bough.'

10 *Then Mary plucked a cherry,
    As red as any blood;
  Then Mary she went homewards
    All with her heavy load.

143

66 THE CHERRY TREE CAROL
PART 2 (CHRISTMAS EVE)

SECOND TUNE

Traditional

Ibid.
(M.S.)

11. As Joseph was a-walking, He heard an an-gel
13. 'He nei-ther shall be clo-thed In pur-ple nor in

sing: 'This night there shall be born On earth our heav'n-ly
pall, But all in fair lin-en As wear the ba-bies

Last verse of Part II begins here.

King;
all.

12. 'He nei-ther shall be born In hou-sen nor in
14. 'He nei-ther shall be rock-ed In sil-ver nor in
15. 'He nei-ther shall be christ-en'd In white wine nor in

hall, Nor in the place of pa-ra-dise, But in an ox-'s stall.
gold, But in a wood-en cra-dle That rocks up-on the mould.
red, But with fair spring wa-ter As we were christ-en-ed.'

66 THE CHERRY TREE CAROL
PART 2 (CHRISTMAS EVE)

THIRD TUNE

Traditional

Ibid.
(M.S.)

11. As Jo - seph was a - walk - ing, He heard an an - gel sing: 'This night there shall be born On earth our heav'n - ly King;

12. 'He nei - ther shall be born In hou - sen nor in hall, Nor in the place of pa - ra - dise, But in an ox - 's stall.

13 'He neither shall be clothèd
    In purple nor in pall,
    But all in fair linen
    As wear the babies all.

14 'He neither shall be rockèd
    In silver nor in gold,
    But in a wooden cradle
    That rocks upon the mould.

15 'He neither shall be christened
    In white wine nor in red,
    But with fair spring water
    As we were christenèd.'

66 THE CHERRY TREE CAROL
PART 3 (LENT: PASSIONTIDE)

FOURTH TUNE

Traditional

Ibid.
(M.S.)

16. Then Ma - ry took her young son, And set him on her knee: Say - ing, 'My dear son, tell me, Tell how this world shall be.'

17. 'O I shall be as dead, mo - ther, As stones are in the wall; O the stones in the streets, mo - ther, Shall sor - row for me all.

18. 'On Eas - ter Day, dear mo - ther, My ris - ing up shall be; O the sun and the moon, mo - ther, Shall both a - rise with me.'

This was one of the most popular carols, and was printed in broadsides in all parts of England. Hone gives a version, 1822, and Sandys another, 1833, identical down to v. 8 with Bullen's. The same legend, with a dialogue no less 'unkind', occurs in *The Coventry Mystery Plays*. Our first tune is from Husk, our second was preserved by Fyfe in his *Carols* of 1860, our third comes from Dr. E. F. Rimbault's *Old English Carols* 1865 and our fourth is also traditional. The whole story of carol-music is summed up in an incident related by Baring-Gould: about 1865 he was teaching carols to a party of mill-girls in the West Riding; 'and amongst them that by Dr. Gauntlett—"Saint Joseph was a-walking"—when they burst out with "Nay! we know one a great deal better nor yond"; and, lifting up their voices, they sang'.

67 SONG OF THE NUNS OF CHESTER
(CHRISTMAS, Medieval)

Chester MS., c. 1425
English words by Denis Stevens
and John A. Parkinson (vv. 4-5)

Ibid.
(arr. John A. Parkinson)

SOLO
CHORUS

1. Qui cre - a - vit coe - - lum,—
1. He who made the star - ry skies,—
2. Jo - seph e - mit pa - ni - cu - lum,—
2. Jo - seph brings a gar - ment there,—
Lul - ly, lul - ly,
By, by, by,— by,

SOLO

lu,———
by,———
Nas - ci - tur in sta - bu - lo,
Sleep - ing in a man - ger— lies,
Ma - ter in - vol - vit pu - e - rum,
Ma - ry wraps up her child so— fair,

CHORUS
SOLO

By, by, by,— by, by,———
Lul - ly, lul - ly, lu,———
Rex qui re - git
Ru - ler of the
Et po - nit in prae -
Rests him while she

CHORUS

sae - cu - lum,—
cen - tu - ries,—
- se - pi - o, —
sings a prayer,
Lul - ly, lul - ly, lu.———
By, by, by,— by, by.———

147

SOLO

3. In - ter a - ni - ma - li - a,____
3. Hum - bly clad, the King of kings,
4. Lac - tat ma - ter Do - mi - ni,____
4. On his mo - ther's breast he lies,____

CHORUS

Lul - ly, lul - ly,
By, by, by,____ by,

lu,____
by,____

SOLO

Ja - cent mun - di gau - di - a,
Joys of heav'n to earth he____ brings,
Os - cu - la - tur par - vu - lum,
She will kiss him if he____ cries,

CHORUS

By, by, by,____ by, by,____
Lul - ly, lul - ly, lu,____

SOLO

Dul - cis su - per
Sweet a - bove all
Et a - do - rat
Ru - ler of the

om - ni - a,____
earth - ly things,
Do - mi - num,____
earth and skies,__

CHORUS

Lul - ly, lul - ly, lu.____
By, by, by,____ by, by.____

5. Ro - ga ma - ter fi - li - um,—⌉
5. *Mo - ther, pray thy sweet child - ing,—*⌋
Lul - ly, lul - ly,

6. In sem - pi - ter - na sae - cu - la,—⌉
6. *Whilst we run this earth - ly race,—*⌋
By, by, by,— by,

lu,———

by,———

Ut det no - bis gau - di - um,⌉
Us e - ter - nal joys to— bring,⌋

In ae - ter - num et ul - tra,⌉
Then through - out all time and— space,⌋

By, by, by,— by, by,———

Lul - ly, lul - ly, lu,———

In per - en - ni
That his prais - es

Det no - bis su - a
May he grant us

glo - ri - a,—⌉
we may sing,—⌋
Lul - ly, lul - ly, lu.———

gau - di - a,—⌉
hope and grace,⌋
By, by, by,— by, by.———

Copyright, 1964, by Oxford University Press

English words (v. 1, 2, 3, 6) by permission of Novello & Co.

The manuscript processional of the nunnery of St. Mary, Chester, c. 1425, (formerly at Bridgewater House and now in the Huntingdon Library, San Marino, California) was printed in facsimile by the Henry Bradshaw Society, vol. xviii, 1899. The plainsong notation of the original lends itself to a variety of rhythmic interpretations. We are indebted to Mr. Denis Stevens for the suggestion of a faux-bourdon harmonization of the refrain.

68 THE TRUTH FROM ABOVE

(GENERAL)

FIRST VERSION

Traditional

Ibid.
(R.V.W.)

1. This is the truth— sent from a - bove, The truth of God,— the God of love, There-fore don't turn me— from your door, But— heark-en all— both— rich— and poor._____ 2. The

first thing which— I do re - late Is that God— did man cre - ate; The— next thing which to— you I'll tell— Wo -man was made with— man— to dwell._____

150

2nd time

3. Thus we were heirs_ to end-less woes, Till
at that sea - son of the year Our

God the Lord did in-ter-pose; And so a pro - mise soon did run That he
blest Re - deem - er did ap-pear; He_ here did live, and_ here did preach, And_

would re - deem_ us_ by_ his Son._ 4. And
ma - ny thou_ sands_

1st time

2nd time

he did teach._____ 5. Thus he in love_ to

cresc.

2nd time

us be-haved, To show us how_ we must be saved; And_

molto rall.

if you want to_ know the way, Be pleas'd to hear_ what_ he_ did say.

colla voce

68 THE TRUTH FROM ABOVE
(GENERAL)

SECOND VERSION

Traditional

Ibid.
(R.V.W.)

Version for unaccompanied singing

SOPRANO
ALTO

1. This is the truth_ sent from a - bove,_ The
2. The first thing which_ I do re - late_

TENOR
BASS

truth of God,_ the God of love,_ There-fore don't turn_ me_
Is that God_ did man cre - ate;_ The_ next thing which_ to_

from your door, But_ heark-en all _ both_ rich_ and_ poor.
you I'll tell— Wo - man was made_ with_ man_ to_ dwell.

3 Thus we were heirs to endless woes,
  Till God the Lord did interpose;
  And so a promise soon did run

  That he would redeem us by his Son.

4 And at that season of the year
  Our blest Redeemer did appear;
  He here did live, and here did preach,
  And many thousands he did teach.

5 Thus he in love to us behaved,
  To show us how we must be saved;
  And if you want to know the way,
  Be pleased to hear what he did say.

Melody and part of text from Mr. W. Jenkins, Kings Pyon, Herefordshire. Melody included by permission of Mrs. Leather. From *Eight Traditional English Carols* (Vaughan Williams), Stainer & Bell. For notes on the text and melody see the *Journal of the Folk Song Society*, iv. 17.
   For another tune and different version of text see Sharp, *English Folk-Carols*, xviii. The version in *A Good Christmas Box* has sixteen verses.

69 THE SAVIOUR'S WORK
(GENERAL : NATIVITY)

Traditional

Ibid.
(E.M.)

1. The babe in Beth - lem's man - ger laid In hum - ble form so low; By won - d'ring an - gels is sur - veyed Through all his scenes of woe :

2. A Sa - viour! sin - ners all a - round Sing, shout the won - drous word; Let ev - 'ry bo - som hail the sound, A Sa - viour! Christ the Lord:

CHORUS

No - well, No - well, now sing a Sa - viour's birth, All

hail his___ com - ing down to earth Who___ rai - ses us to___ heav'n!

3 For not to sit on David's throne
   With worldly pomp and joy,
   He came on earth for sin to atone,
   And Satan to destroy:

   Nowell, etc.

4 To preach the word of life divine,
   And feed with living bread,
   To heal the sick with hand benign,
   And raise to life the dead:

   Nowell, etc.

5 *He preached, he suffered, bled and died,
   Uplift 'twixt earth and skies;
   In sinners' stead was crucified,
   For sin a sacrifice:

   Nowell, etc.

6 *Well may we sing a Saviour's birth,
   Who need the grace so given,
   And hail his coming down to earth,
   Who raises us to heaven:

   Nowell, etc.

In the Staffordshire *A Good Christmas Box*, 1847, without the
chorus, which is given, with the tune, in Rimbault's *Old English Carols*, 1865.

70 JOYS SEVEN
(GENERAL)

Traditional

Ibid.
(M.S.)

Solo or semi-chorus

SOPRANO
ALTO

1. The first ⎱
2. The next ⎰ good joy that Ma - ry had, It was the joy of

TENOR
BASS

⎰ one; ____ To see the bless - ed Je - sus Christ When
⎱ two; ____ To see her own son, Je - sus Christ, To

CHORUS

he was first ___ her son: ____ When he was first her
make the lame ___ to go: ____ To make the lame to

When ____
To ____

son, *good man:_ And bless - ed may he be,* ____ *Both* ____
go,

Fa - ther, Son, and Ho - ly Ghost, To all e - ter - ni - ty. ____

3 The next good joy that Mary had,
    It was the joy of three;
  To see her own son, Jesus Christ,
    To make the blind to see:

4 The next good joy that Mary had,
    It was the joy of four;
  To see her own son, Jesus Christ,
    To read the bible o'er:

5 The next good joy that Mary had,
    It was the joy of five;
  To see her own son, Jesus Christ,
    To bring the dead alive:

6 The next good joy that Mary had,
    It was the joy of six;
  To see her own son, Jesus Christ,
    Upon the crucifix:

7 The next good joy that Mary had,
    It was the joy of seven;
  To see her own son, Jesus Christ,
    To wear the crown of heaven:

3. Adding 'To make the blind to see, good man', and so on in all verses.

Some versions have for v. 6 'to bear the crucifix'. The version in Hill's MS., in another metre, gives the seeing Jesus on the rood as the third joy: his five are the Annunciation, Nativity, Crucifixion, Harrowing of Hell, Ascension. The Sloane MS. 2593 of the fifteenth century also gives the witnessing of the Crucifixion as a 'joy of great might'. This carol was one of the most popular and was annually reprinted in eighteenth-century broadsides all over England. In late eighteenth-century and nineteenth-century sheets it is sometimes extended to twelve. A melody was noted by Cecil Sharp with a Ten Joy version (8, 'To bring the croked straight', 9, 'Turn water into wine', 10, 'Bring up ten gentlemen') from Mrs. Duddridge at Mark, Somerset—*Folk Songs from Somerset* (No. 125) and *English Folk Carols*. A Gloucestershire version gives Twelve Joys (10, 'To write with a golden pen', 11, 'To have the keys of heaven', 12, 'To have the keys of hell'); Husk gives Twelve from a Newcastle sheet, with many variants (e.g. 10, 'To write without a pen'). The Seven Joy versions are older and less corrupt descendants of the Seven Joys of the Sloane MS. Bramley & Stainer (1871) printed the traditional air here given. W. J. Phillips in *Carols* (c. 1890) stated that he remembered the unemployed, c. 1850, tramping with shovels through the London snow and singing to the tune, 'We've got no work to do-oo-oo'. We can corroborate this for a later period, c. 1890, only they sang, 'We're all froze out'.

71 MY DANCING DAY
PART 1 (GENERAL)

Traditional

Ibid.
(M.S.)

1. To - mor-row shall be_ my dan - cing day: I would_ my
2. Then was_ I born of a vir - gin pure, Of her_ I

true_ love did_ so chance To_ see the le - gend
took flesh - ly_ sub - stance; Thus_ was I knit to

of_ my play, } To call my true_ love to_ my
man's na - ture, }

Sing O my_ love, O_ my love, my

love, my love; This have I done_ for my_ true love.

Part 2 (Lent: Passiontide)

3 In a manger laid and wrapped I was,
   So very poor, this was my chance,
   Betwixt an ox and a silly poor ass,
   To call my true love to my dance:

   Sing O my love etc.

4 Then afterwards baptized I was;
   The Holy Ghost on me did glance,
   My Father's voice heard from above,
   To call my true love to my dance:

   Sing O my love etc.

5 Into the desert I was led,
   Where I fasted without substánce;
   The devil bade me make stones my bread,
   To have me break my true love's dance:

   Sing O my love etc.

6 The Jews on me they made great suit,
   And with me made great variance,
   Because they loved darkness rather than light,
   To call my true love to my dance:

   Sing O my love etc.

7 For thirty pence Judas me sold,
   His covetousness for to advance;
   'Mark whom I kiss, the same do hold,'
   The same is he shall lead the dance:

   Sing O my love etc.

Part 3 (Passiontide: Easter: Ascension)

8 Before Pilate the Jews me brought,
   Where Barabbas had deliveránce;
   They scourgèd me and set me at nought,
   Judged me to die to lead the dance:

   Sing O my love etc.

9 Then on the cross hangèd I was,
   Where a spear to my heart did glance;
   There issued forth both water and blood,
   To call my true love to my dance:

   Sing O my love etc.

10 Then down to hell I took my way
   For my true love's deliverance,
   And rose again on the third day,
   Up to my true love and the dance:

   Sing O my love etc.

11 Then up to heaven I did ascend,
   Where now I dwell in sure substánce
   On the right hand of God, that man
   May come unto the general dance:

   Sing O my love etc.

Words and melody from Sandys, 1833. In many broadsides. This is probably based on a secular song, but the interweaving of the two love motives is as ancient and widespread as the association of religion with the dance. The text seems to go back earlier than the seventeenth century.

72 WONDROUS WORKS
PART 1 (GENERAL)

Traditional

Ibid.
(M.S.)

1. When Jesus Christ was twelve years old, As holy scripture plain-ly told, He then dis-pu-ted brave and bold A-mongst the learn-ed doc-tors:

2. At thir-ty years he then be-gan To preach the gos-pel un-to man, And all Ju-dae-a won-dered then To hear his heav'n-ly doc-trine:

Then praise the Lord both high and low, 'Cause he his won-drous works doth shew, That we at last to heav'n might go, Where Christ in glo-ry reign-eth.

3 The woman's son, that dead did lie,
   When Christ our Saviour passèd by,
   He rose to life immediately,
      To her great joy and comfort:

   Then praise the Lord etc.

4 Likewise he healed the lepers ten,
   Whose bodies were full filthy then;
   And there returnèd back but one
      Him humble thanks to render:

   Then praise the Lord etc.

5 *More of his heavenly might to shew,
   Himself upon the sea did go;
   And there was none that e'er did so,
      But only Christ our Saviour:

   Then praise the Lord etc.

PART 2 (PASSIONTIDE: EASTER: ASCENSION)

6 When they bereaved his life so good,
   The moon was turnèd into blood,
   The earth and Temple shaking stood,
      And graves full wide did open:

   Then praise the Lord etc.

7 Then some of them that stood thereby
   With voices loud began to cry:
   'This was the Son of God truly,'
      ♪ | ♩ ♪ ♪
   Without any fear or doubting:

   Then praise the Lord etc.

8 For, as he said, it came so plain,
   That in three days he rose again;
   Although he suffered bitter pain,
      Both heaven and earth he conquered:

   Then praise the Lord etc.

9 Then afterwards ascended he
   To heaven in glorious majesty;
   With him God grant us all to be
      In heaven with him rejoicing:

   Then praise the Lord etc.

As in Gilbert, 1822 (15 verses), with two
corrections from Sandys (1833), who also gives the tune.

2. FOREIGN CAROLS
WITH THEIR TRADITIONAL WORDS TRANSLATED

73 DUTCH CAROL
(CHRISTMAS)

Tr. R.C. Trevelyan

Dutch, 1599
(arr. Julius Röntgen)

1. A child— is born— in Beth - le - hem: A - wait - eth him
2. The Son took up - on him hu - ma - ni - ty, That to— the

all— Je - ru - sa - lem.
Fa - ther thus draws nigh:

A - mor, a - mor, a-

-mor, a - mor, a - mor! quam dul - cis est a - mor!

3 The angels above were singing then,
  Below were rejoicing the shepherd men:

  Amor, etc.

4 Now let us all with the angels sing,
  Yea, now let our hearts for gladness spring:

  Amor, etc.

1. *Amor, &c.*—Love! how sweet is love!
  We owe the original of this carol, 'Een kint gheboren in Bethlehem' to the kindness of Professor Röntgen in Holland.

74 FLEMISH CAROL
(CHRISTMAS AND NEW YEAR)

Tr. R.C. Trevelyan

Old Flemish
(arr. Julius Röntgen)

1. A lit - tle child on the earth has been born, A lit - tle
2. He came to earth but no home did he find, He came to
3. He came to earth for the sake of us all, He came to

child on the earth has been born; He came to the earth for the
earth but no home did he find, He came to earth and its
earth for the sake of us all And wish - es us all a

sake of us all, He came to the earth for the sake of us all!
cross did he bear, He came to earth and its cross did he bear.
hap - py New Year, And wish - es us all a hap - py New Year.

As in the case of No. 73, we owe the original,
'Er is een kindeken geboren op d'aard', to Professor Röntgen.

75 BETHLEHEM
DANS CETTE ETABLE
(CHRISTMAS)

Fléchier tr. Maurice F. Bell

French
(arr. Charles Gounod)

1. In that poor sta - ble How charm-ing Je - sus lies, Words are not
2. See here God's pow - er In weak-ness for - ti-fies This in - fant

a - ble To fath - om his em - prise!__ No pal - ace of a
hour__ Of Love's e - pi - phan - ies! __ Our foe is now de -

king__ Can show so rare a thing__ In his - to - ry or
-spoiled,__ The wiles of hell are foiled;__ On earth there grows a

fa - ble As that of which we sing In that poor sta - - ble.
Flow - er Pure, un - de - filed, un - soiled— See here God's pow - - er!

3   Though far from knowing
  The babe's divinity,
    Mine eyes are growing
  To see his majesty;
  For lo! the new-born child
  Upon me sweetly smiled,
    The gift of faith bestowing;
  Thus I my Lord descry,
    Though far from knowing.

4   No more affliction!
  For God endures our pains;
    In crucifixion
  The Son victorious reigns.
  For us the sufferer brings
  Salvation in his wings;
    To win our souls' affection,
  Could he, the King of kings,
    Know more affliction?

DANS cette étable
Que Jésus est charmant,
  Qu'il est aimable
Dans cet abaissement!
Que d'attraits à la fois!
Tous les palais des rois
  N'ont rien de comparable
Aux charmes que je vois
  Dans cette étable.

2   Que sa puissance
Paraît bien en ce jour,
  Malgré l'enfance
Où l'a réduit l'amour!
Notre ennemi dompté,
L'enfer déconcerté,
  Font voir qu'en sa naissance
Rien n'est si redouté
  Que sa puissance.

3   Sans le connaître,
Dans sa divinité
  Je vois paraître
Toute sa majesté;
Dans cet enfant qui naît,
À son aspect qui plaît,
  Je découvre mon maître
Et je sens ce qu'il est
  Sans le connaître.

4   *Plus de misère!
Un Dieu souffre pour nous
  Et de son père
Appaise le courroux;
C'est en notre faveur
Qu'il naît dans la douleur;
  Pouvait-il pour nous plaire
Unir à sa grandeur
  Plus de misère?

We give the original as well as a translation of this French carol, which is often called Gounod's 'Bethlehem' because the traditional tune was arranged by C. F. Gounod (1818-93).

76 ES IST EIN' ROS'
(*There is a flower*)
(CHRISTMAS)

German, 15th century
English words by
Ursula Vaughan Williams

Ibid.
(arr. Michael Praetorius)

1. There is a flow-er spring-ing From ten - der
From Ed - en beau-ty bring-ing From Jes - - se's

ten - der roots
Jes - se's stem

roots it grows,
stem a rose.
On his green branch it blows:— A

— it grows,
— a rose,

bud that in cold win - ter At mid - night— will— un - close.

mid-night will— un - close.

The barring of this tune is necessarily irregular. But its performance will
be found to be easy if it is remembered that the time-value of a crotchet
is the same throughout.

2 Pure Mary, maiden holy,
    The dream by prophets seen,
Who in a stable lowly
    Above her child did lean
    So gentle and serene:
This was Esaias' vision,
    The tree of living green.

3 To Mary, rose of heaven,
    With loving hearts we say
Let our sins be forgiven,
    And grief be turned away
    Upon this Christmas Day:
To Jesus, child of winter,
    For grace and hope we pray.

Es ist ein' Ros' entsprungen
    Aus einer Wurzel zart,
Als uns die Alten sungen:
    Aus Jesse kam die Art;
    Und hat ein Blümlein bracht,
Mitten im kalten Winter,
    Wohl zu der halben Nacht.

2 Das Röslein das ich meine,
    Davon Esaias sagt,
Hat uns gebracht alleine
    Marie die reine Magd.
    Aus Gottes ew'gem Rat
Hat sie ein Kind geboren,
    Wohl zu der halben Nacht.

The fifteenth-century words and melody are in the *Speierschen
Gesangbuch*, Cologne, 1600; the setting by Praetorius in *Musae Sioniae*, 1609.

77 SONG OF THE CRIB
JOSEPH LIEBER, JOSEPH MEIN
(CHRISTMAS)

Tr. N.S.T.

German, 15th century
(R.V.W.)

VOICES IN UNISON

Moderately fast

ACCPT.

1. Jo - seph dear - est, Jo - seph mine, Help me cra - dle the child di - vine; God re - ward thee and all that's thine In par - a - dise, So prays the mo - ther Ma - ry.

2. Glad - ly, dear one, la - dy mine, Help I cra - dle this child of thine; God's own light on us both shall shine In par - a - dise, As prays the mo - ther Ma - ry.

Servant(1) 3. Peace to all that have good-will! God, who heav-en and earth doth fill, Comes to turn us a - way from ill, And lies so still With - in the crib of Ma - ry.

Servant(2) 4. All shall come and bow the knee; Wise and hap-py their souls shall be, Lov - ing such a di - vin - i - ty, As all may see In Je - sus, Son of Ma - ry.

See overleaf for Chorus

167

CHORUS

He came a - mong us at Christ - mas - tide, At Christ - mas - tide, In

Beth - le - hem; Men shall bring him from far and wide Love's

di - a - dem: Je - sus, Je - sus,

Lo, he comes, and loves, and saves, and frees us!

Servant(3) 5. Now is born Em-man-u-el, Pro-phe-sied once by E-ze-ki-el, Pro-mis'd Ma-ry by Ga-bri-el— Ah, who can tell Thy prais-es, Son of Ma-ry!

Servant(4) 6. Thou my la-zy heart hast stirred, Thou, the Fa-ther's e-ter-nal Word, Great-er than aught_ that ear hath heard, Thou ti-ny bird Of love, thou Son of Ma-ry.

Servant(1) 7. Sweet and love-ly lit-tle one, Thou prince-ly, beau-ti-ful, God's own Son, With-out thee all of us were un-done; Our love is won By thine, O Son of Ma-ry.

Servant(2) 8. Lit-tle man, and God in-deed, Lit-tle and poor, thou art all we need; We will fol-low where thou dost lead, And we will heed Our bro-ther, born of Ma-ry.

(Chorus)

For German text and editorial note see overleaf.

169

JOSEPH lieber, Joseph mein,
Hilf mir wiegen mein Kindelein;
Gott der will dein Lohner sein
    Im Himmelreich, der Jungfrau Sohn Maria.

Er ist erschienen am heut'gen Tag,
Am heut'gen Tag in Israel:
Der Maria verkündigt ist
Durch Gabriel.
*   Eya, eya,*
*   Jesum Christ hat uns geborn Maria.*

2 Gerne, liebe Muhme mein,
  Helf ich dir wiegen dein Kindelein
  Dass Gott müsse mein Lohner sein
     Im Himmelreich, der Jungfrau Sohn Maria.

Er ist erschienen usw.

3 Nun freu' dich, christenliche Schar
  Der himmelische König klar
  Nahm die Menschheit offenbar
     Den uns gebar die reine Magd Maria.

Er ist erschienen usw.

4 O ew'gen Vaters ew'ges Wort
  Wahr Gott, wahr Mensch, der Tugend Hort
  In Himmel und Erde hie und dort
     Der Sölden Pfort, die aufgetan Maria.

Er ist erschienen usw.

'Joseph lieber, Joseph mein, Hilf mir wiegen mein Kindelein' occurs in a MS. at Leipzig University, *c.* 1500, as part of a mystery play acted in church around the crib. It would make today a beautiful little Christmas play for children, Mary and Joseph singing vv. 1 and 2, and then the children singing the chorus. In the old arrangement the chorus was not sung after every verse; the remaining verses can be sung by one or more men and women (servants of the inn), each verse (or the alternate verses) being followed by the chorus. There are versions in German and Latin ('Resonet in laudibus'), some without the chorus, in Johann Walther's *Gesangbuch,* 1544, *Piae Cantiones* and elsewhere. The tune was used in polyphonic settings by Lassus, Handl, Praetorius and many others, and Brahms employs it as a viola obbligato in his song 'Geistliches Wiegenlied'. Our version is that of the *Mainzer Cantual,* 1605, the harmonies being those of *The English Hymnal* (612) and *Songs of Praise* (700), 'Resonet in laudibus' being there set to new words.

78 PERSONENT HODIE

SING ALOUD ON THIS DAY!

(CHRISTMAS: EPIPHANY)

Piae Cantiones, 1582
Tr. John A. Parkinson

German, 1360
(arr. Gustav Holst)

1. Per - so - nent ho - di - e Vo - ces pu - er - u - lae, Lau - dan - tes ju - cun - de Qui no - bis est
2. In mun - do nas - ci - tur, Pan - nis in - vol - vi - tur, Prae - se - pi po - ni - tur Sta - bu - lo bru -
3. Ma - gi tres ve - ne - runt, Par - vu - lum in - qui - runt, Par - vu - lum in - qui - runt, Stel - lu - lam se -
4. Om - nes cle - ric - u - li, Par - i - ter pu - e - ri, Can - tent ut an - ge - li: Ad - ven - is - ti

na - - tus, Sum - mo De - o da - - tus,
-to - - rum, Rec - tor su - per - no - - rum.
-quen - - do, Ip - sum a - do - ran - - do,
mun - - do, Lau - des ti - bi fun - - do.

Et de vir - vir - vir, Et de vir - vir - vir,
Per - di - dit, dit, dit, Per - di - dit, dit, dit,
Au - rum, thus, thus, thus, Au - rum, thus, thus, thus,
Id - e - o, o, o, Id - e - o, o, o,

Et de vir - gi - ne - o ven - tre pro - cre - a - tus.
Per - di - dit spo - li - a prin - ceps in - fer - no - rum.
Au - rum, thus, et myrr - ham e - i of - fe - ren - do.
Id - e - o glo - ri - a in ex - cel - sis De - o!

Copyright, 1924, by Gustav Holst

This carol is here printed with its original Latin words from *Piae Cantiones*, 1582, to make our book more complete. V. 1, in the original book, 'virgineo' is printed 'vir ij ij gineo' under the music to show the repetition at the end of each verse. For note on *Piae Cantiones* see No. 141.

(English translation of PERSONENT HODIE)

Moderato maestoso

1. Sing a - loud on this day! Child - ren all
2. Now a child he is born, Swath - ing bands
3. From the far Or - i - ent Guid - ing star
4. All must join him to praise; Men and boys

raise the lay. Cheer - ful - ly we and they Hast - en to a -
him a - dorn, Man - ger bed he'll not scorn, Ox and ass are
wise men sent; Him to seek their in - tent, Lord of all cre -
voi - ces raise On this day of all days; An - gel voi - ces

-dore thee, Sent from high - est glo - ry, For us born,
near him; We as Lord re - vere him, And the vain,
- a - tion; Kneel in ad - o - ra - tion. Gifts of gold,
ring - ing, Christ - mas ti - dings bring - ing. Join we all,

born, born, For us born, born, born, For us born
vain, vain, And the vain, vain, vain, And the vain
gold, gold, Gifts of gold, gold, gold, Gifts of gold,
all, all, Join we all, all, all, Join we all,

on this morn Of the Vir - gin Ma - ry.
powers of hell Spoiled of prey now fear him.
frank - in - cense, Myrrh for their ob - la - tion.
'Glo - ri - a In ex - cel - sis' sing - ing.

79 QUEM PASTORES

SHEPHERDS LEFT THEIR FLOCKS A-STRAYING

(CHRISTMAS: EPIPHANY)

German, 14th century
English words by Imogen Holst

Ibid.
(R.V.W.)

1. Quem pas-to-res lau-da-ve-re, Qui-bus
1. Shep-herds left their flocks_ a-stray-ing, God's_ com-

an-ge-li dix-e-re, Ab-sit vo-bis
-mand_ with joy o-bey-ing, When they heard the

jam ti-me-re, Na-tus est_ rex glo-ri-ae.
an-gel say-ing: 'Christ is born_ in Beth-le-hem.'

2 Ad quem magi ambulabant,
  Aurum, thus, myrrham portabant,
  Immolabant haec sincere
    Nato regi gloriae.

3 Christo regi, Deo nato,
  Per Mariam nobis dato,
  Merito resonet vere
    Laus, honor et gloria.

2 *Wise Men came from far, and saw him:*
  Knelt in homage to adore him;
  Precious gifts they laid before him:
    Gold and frankincense and myrrh.

3 *Let us now in every nation*
  Sing his praise with exultation.
  All the world shall find salvation
    In the birth of Mary's Son.

The carol occurs in V. Triller, 1555, *Leisentritt*, 1567, in Schein's *Cantional*, 1627, and elsewhere.
According to tradition this carol was sung, line by line, by four separate groups of choir-boys.

80 THREE KINGS
(INNOCENTS: EPIPHANY)

Tr. Robert Graves

Flemish
(M.S.)

1. Three kings are here, both weal-thy and wise, Come ri-ding far o-ver the
2. God's an-gel speaks Saint Jo-seph a-nigh: 'With Je-sus thy charge in-to
3. He-rod be-trays these in-no-cent lives Both young-er and el-der to

snow-co-vered ice; Roy-al in throng, No-ble in song,— They
far E-gypt fly. Stay not nor stand; He-rod's at hand.' The
lan-ces and knives. Who can dare tell Mur-der so fell?— These

search for the child, the Re-deem-er of wrong; With tam-bours and drums they go
ass hast-ens pant-ing; the hot de-sert sand Has res-cued our Sa-viour from
pret-ty young chil-dren in an-guish of hell Were mar-tyred to-ge-ther his

sound-ing a-long, With tam-bours and drums they go sound-ing a-long.
He-rod's ill band, Has res-cued our Sa-viour from He-rod's ill band.
an-ger to quell, Were mar-tyred to-ge-ther his an-ger to quell.

A translation of 'De Drie Koningen', an old Flemish carol.

81 TORCHES
(CHRISTMAS)

Tr. J. B. Trend

Galician
(arr. from Pedrell)

1. Torch - es, torch - es, run with torch - es All the way to
2. Ah, ro - ro, ro - ro, my ba - by, Ah, ro - ro, my
3. Sing, my friends, and make you mer - ry, Joy and mirth and

Beth - le - hem! Christ is born and now lies
love, ro - ro; Sleep you well, my heart's own
joy a - gain; Lo, he lives, the King of

sleep - ing; Come and sing your song to him!
dar - ling, While we sing you our ro - ro.
hea - ven, Now and ev - er - more. A - men.

A Spanish carol from Galicia, 'Villancico de Navidad'. The melody is from Pedrell, *Cancionero musical;* the words are translated from the *Cancionero popular gallego* by J. Pérez Ballesteros. The second verse may be repeated at the end.

La Monnoye
Tr. O.B.C.

Burgundian
(M.S.)

VERSES 1, 3

SOPRANO
ALTO

1. Wil - lie, take your lit - tle
3. God and man are now be - -
1. Guil - laume prends ton tam - bou - -
3. L'homme et Dieu sont plus d'ac - -

TENOR
BASS

(FOR BOTH TEXTS) Pat - a - pan, pat - a - pan, pat - a -

drum, With your whis - tle, Rob - - - in,
-come More at one than fife and
- rin, toi, prends ta flû - te, Ro - - -
-cord Que la flûte et le tam -

-pan, pat - a - pan, pat - a - pan, pat - a - pan, pat - a -

come! When we hear the fife and
drum. When you hear the fife and
- bin; Au son de ces in - stru -
-bour. Au son de ces in - stru -

-pan, pat - a - pan, pat - a - pan, pat - a - pan, pat - a -

VERSE 2

Tu - re - lu, tu - re - lu, tu - re -

2. Thus the men of old - en
2. C'é - tait la mode aut - re -

Pat - a - pan, pat - a - pan, pat - a -

-lu, tu - re - lu, tu - re - lu, tu - re - lu, tu - re -

days Loved the King of kings to
-fois de lou - er le Roi des

- pan, pat - a - pan, pat - a - pan, pat - a - pan, pat - a -

- lu, tu - re - lu, tu - re - lu, tu - re - lu, tu - re

praise: When they hear the fife and
rois, Au son de ces in - stru -

- pan, pat - a - pan, pat - a - pan, pat - a - pan, pat - a -

---

-lu, tu-re-lu, tu-re-lu, tu-re-lu, lu,
drum,
- ments,
Tu-re-lu-re-lu, pat-a-pat-a-
-pan, pat-a-pan, pat-a-pan, pat-a-pan, pat-a-

lu, tu-re-lu, lu, lu, tu-re-lu, tu-re-
When they hear the fife and
Au son de ces in-stru-
-pan, pat-a-pan, pat-a-pan, pat-a-pan, pat-a-

-lu, tu-re-lu, tu-re-lu, tu-re-lu, tu-re-lu.
drum, Sure our chil-dren won't be dumb!
- ments Il nous en faut faire au-tant.
-pan, pat-a-pan, pat-a-pan, pat-a-pan, pan, pan.

D.C.
for v. 3

(May be sung a semitone higher)

The French spelling has been modernized.

It may be worth while to print the first verse of the original dialect noël, which illustrates the genial nature of those old French carols that were not rewritten in an age of less spontaneous faith: 'Guillô, pran ton tamborin. | Toi, pran tai fleùte Rôbin; Au son de cés instruman, | Turelurelu patapatapan; Au son de cés instruman. | Je diron Noei gaiman. The carol is printed by F. Fertiault, Noëls Bourgignons de Bernard de la Monnoye, 1842. Bernard lived from 1641 to 1728.

The *tambourin* is a small elongated drum, hung from the shoulders, and played originally with the hands.

Sandys got hold of this carol a century ago; and the original words were reprinted, 1907, by H. J. L. Masse and C. Kennedy Scott in their first *Book of Old Carols*. As the tune runs quickly, it may be well to repeat one or more verses.

180

83 CONGAUDEAT
(CHRISTMAS: NEW YEAR: EPIPHANY)

Piae Cantiones, 1582
Tr. Maurice F. Bell

Ibid.
(harm. Geoffrey Shaw)

1. With mer — — — ry heart let all — re - joice — in one; — The mo - ther-maid hath now — brought forth — her son — } *In Beth - le - hem.* —

2. An an — — — gel's voice — de - clared the Sa - viour's birth, — Glo - ry — to God, good- will — and peace — on earth: } *In Beth - le - hem.* —

3 The shepherds sped to see this wondrous thing
And found the babe, the which is Christ our King:

In Bethlehem.

4 Both ox and ass, adoring in the byre,
In mute acclaim pay homage to our Sire:

In Bethlehem.

5 As custom was, the babe when eight days old
Received his name of Jesus, long foretold:

In Bethlehem.

6 Three kings bowed low to infant majesty
And brought three gifts to hail the Trinity:

In Bethlehem.

7 Now bless we Christ, eternal glory's King,
And Christ bless us, as to his praise we sing:

In Bethlehem.

The words and melody of 'Congaudeat turba fidelium' occur in the Swedish *Piae Cantiones* (1582) (see note to No. 141); but the tune is much older than this; an early form of it is found in a twelfth-century MS., from Apt, near Avignon, printed in the *Revue du Chant Grégorien* for September 1902.

84 THE CRADLE
EIN KINDLEIN IN DER WIEGEN
(NATIVITY)

Austrian, 1649
Tr. Robert Graves

Ibid.
(M.S.)

1. He smiles with-in his cra - dle, A babe with face so bright It beams most like a mir - ror A-gainst a blaze of light: This babe so burn-ing bright.

2. This babe we now de-clare to you Is Je - sus Christ our Lord; He brings both peace and heart-i-ness: Haste, haste with one ac-cord To feast with Christ our Lord.

This babe
To feast

3 And who would rock the cradle
  Wherein this infant lies,
Must rock with easy motion
  And watch with humble eyes,
  Like Mary pure and wise.

4 O Jesus, dearest babe of all
  And dearest babe of mine,
Thy love is great, thy limbs are small.
  O, flood this heart of mine
  With overflow from thine!

EIN Kindlein in der Wiegen,
  Ein kleines Kindelein,
Das gleisst gleich wie ein Spiegel
  Nach Adelichem Schein,
  Das kleine Kindelein.

2 Das Kindlein das wir meinen
  Das heisst Herr Jesus Christ
Das verleih uns Fried und Innigkeit
  Wohl heut zu dieser Frist,
  Das geb Herr Jesus Christ.

3 Und wer das Kindlein will umtragen,
  Das seelig Kindelein,
Der muss ein keusch Herz haben
  Gleich wie ein Jungfrau rein,
  Maria der Mutter sein.

4 Maria, wir wöllen dich bitten
  Mit deinem Kindelein
Du wöllest uns nicht verlassen
  Wöllest allzeit bei uns sein
  Mit deinem Kindelein.

Translation of 'Ein Kindlein in der Wiegen'. Words and melody from D. G. Corner's *Geistliche Nachtigal*, Vienna, 1649. Wackernagel also gives it from an Augsburg print of 1590.

85 PUER NATUS
(NATIVITY)

Tr. N.S.T.

German, 16th century
(M.S.)

1. A boy was born in Beth - le - hem, in Beth - -
2. For low he lay with - in a stall, with - in

- - le - hem;___ Re - joice for that, Je - ru - sa -
___ a stall,___ Who rules for ev - er ov - er

- lem!
all: Al - le - lu - ya, al - le - - - lu - ya.

3 He let himself a servant be,
    a servant be,
That all mankind he might set free:

    Alleluya.

4 Then praise the Word of God who came,
    the Word of God who came,
To dwell within a human frame:

    Alleluya.

5 And praised be God in threefold might,
    And glory bright,
Eternal, good, and infinite!

    Alleluya.

If both versions are used together it is suggested that the alternative be sung, slower, to the last verse.

This melody for 'Ein kind geborn zu Bethlehem' ('Puer natus in Bethlehem') is in L. Lossius's *Psalmodia*, 1553, the Ingolstadt *Obsequiale*, 1570, and in many German books of the seventeenth century: it is really the descant of an older melody which it has supplanted.

ALTERNATIVE VERSION (as harmonized by J. S. Bach)

SOPRANO
ALTO

1. A   boy   was   born   in   Beth - le - hem,   in
2. For   low   he   lay   with - in___   a   stall,   with -
5. And   praised   be   God   in   three - fold might,   And

TENOR
BASS

Beth - - - le - hem;   Re - joice   for that,   Je - ru - sa -
- in___   a   stall,   Who rules   for ev - er   ov - er
glo - - - ry bright,   E - ter - nal, good, and in - fi -

- lem!
all: Al - le - lu - ya,   al - le - - - lu - ya.
- nite!

EIN Kind geborn zu Bethlehem, zu Bethlehem;
Des freuet sich Jerusalem!

Alleluya.

2 Hier liegt es in dem Krippelein, dem Krippelein
Ohn' Ende ist die Herrschaft sein,

Alleluya.

3 Gelobt seist du, Herr Jesu Christ, Herr Jesu Christ,
Der du als Mensch geboren bist.

Alleluya.

4 Zu dieser heiligen Weihnachtszeit, Weihnachtszeit
Sei Gott der Herr gebenedeit.

Alleluya.

185

86 IN DULCI JUBILO
(NATIVITY)

Tr. S. P.

German, 14th century
(harm. Bartholomew Gesius, 1601)

VERSES 1, 2, & 3

Allegro

SOPRANO
ALTO

1. *In dul-ci ju-bi-lo*_____ Now sing with hearts a-glow!_____
2. *O Je-su, par-vu-le,*_____ For thee I long al-way;_____

TENOR
BASS

Our de-light and plea-sure Lies *in prae-se-pi-o,*_____ Like
Com-fort my heart's blind-ness, *O pu-er op-ti-me,*_____ With

sun-shine is our trea-sure *Ma-tris in gre-mi-o.*_____ Like
all thy lov-ing-kind-ness, *O prin-ceps glo-ri-ae.*_____ With

*Al - pha es et O!*_____ *Al - pha es et O!*
*Tra - he me post te!*_____ *Tra - he me post te!*

The small notes in the last two bars are added to
preserve the usual version of the tune, and may be used if preferred.

3 *O Patris caritas!*
  O Nati lenitas!
    Deeply were we stainèd
  Per nostra crimina;
    But thou for us hast gainèd
  Coelorum gaudia.
  O that we were there!

4 *Ubi sunt gaudia*
  In any place but there?
    There are angels singing
  Nova cantica,
    And there the bells are ringing
  In Regis curia.
  O that we were there!

In dulci jubilo
Nun singet und seid froh!
  Unsers Herzens Wonne
Leit *in praesepio,*
  Und leuchtet als die Sonne
Matris in gremio.
Alpha es et O!

3 *O Patris caritas!*
  O Nati lenitas!
    Wir wären all verloren
  Per nostra crimina
    So hat er uns erworben
  Coelorum gaudia
  Eia, wären wir da!

2 *O Jesu parvule*
  Nach dir ist mir so weh!
    Tröst mir mein Gemüte
  O puer optime
    Durch alle deine Güte
  O princeps gloriae.
  Trahe me post te!

4 *Ubi sunt gaudia*
  Nirgend mehr denn da!
    Da die Engel singen
  Nova cantica,
    Und die Schellen klingen
  In regis curia.
  Eia, wären wir da!

Setting by J.S. BACH

VERSE 4
Maestoso

4. U - bi sunt gau - di - a _____ In an - y place but there? _____

There are an - gels sing - - ing No - - va can - ti -

There are _ an - gels _ sing - ing

-ca,_____ And there the bells_ are ring - -ing *In*
Re - gis cu - ri - a._____ O that we were
there!

Re - gis cu - ri - a._____ O that_ we_ were_
Re - gis cu - ri - a._____ O_ that we_____ were

there! O_____ that we were there!
there!_ O_____ that we_ were_ there!

O_____ that we_ were there!_

1. *In dulci jubilo*—In sweet shouting, or jubilation. *In praesepio*—in a manger. *Matris*, &c.—In his mother's lap. *Alpha*, &c.—Thou art Alpha and Omega. 2. *O Jesu parvule*—O tiny Jesus. *O puer optime*—O best of boys. *O princeps gloriae*—O prince of glory. *Trahe*, &c.—Draw me after thee. 3. *O Patris*, &c.—O love of the Father. *O Nati*, &c.—O gentleness of the Son. *Per nostra*, &c.—Through our crimes. *Coelorum*, &c.—The joys of the heavens. 4. *Ubi sunt*, &c.—Where are joys? *Nova*, &c.—New songs. *In Regis*, &c.—In the court of the King.

This famous old German macaronic carol was first translated into English by John Wedderburn in his *Gude and Godly Ballates, c.* 1540, 'In dulci jubilo, Now let us sing with mirth and jo[y]', irregular, in three stanzas. Other translations are—*Lyra Davidica*, 1708, Sir J. Bowring, 1825, &c. R. L. de Pearsall (1795-1856) and G. R. Woodward in the *Cowley Carol Book* follow the tune correctly. The music only allows us to use three of Wedderburn's lines (21 and 28 in part, and 23) in this new rendering.

Because of the importance of this carol, we append the original old German lines: 1. Nu singet und seyt fro: Unsers herzens wonne Leyt: Und leuchtet als die sonne. 2. Nach dir ist mir so we: Tröst mir myn gemüte: Durch aller juncfrawen güte. 3. Wir weren all verloren: So hat er uns erworben: Eya, wär wir da! 4. Nirgend mer denn da: Da die engel singen: Und die schellen klingen: Eya, wär wir da! But there are many variants, old and new, e.g. in v. 2 the fifteenth-century line is modernized by Vehe to 'Durch alle deine Güte'.

The fourteenth-century melody occurs, with the words, in a MS. at Leipzig University Library, which belongs to the beginning of the fifteenth century. The developed form of the melody is in Michael Vehe's *Gesangbuch*, Leipzig, 1537, and in Witzel's *Psaltes Ecclesiasticus*, Cologne, 1550. In Babst's *Gesangbuch*, Leipzig, 1545, the last hymn-book produced for Luther and representing his final text-editorship, the third stanza, doubtless by Luther himself, 'O Patris caritas', is substituted for an earlier one. The melody and versions of the words occur in many other books, including *Piae Cantiones*, 1582, with a Swedish translation.

The original words are said by a fourteenth-century writer to have been sung by angels to Henry Suso (d. 1366), the mystic, who was drawn in thereby to dance with his celestial visitors.

87 ROCKING
(NATIVITY)

Tr. O.B.C.

Czech (M.S.)

1. Lit - tle Je - sus, sweet - ly__ sleep, do not__ stir;
2. Ma - ry's lit - tle ba - by,__ sleep, sweet - ly __ sleep,

We will__ lend a__ coat of__ fur,
Sleep in__ com - fort,__ slum - ber__ deep; We will rock you,

rock you, rock you, We will rock you, rock you, rock you:

See the fur to keep you__ warm, Snug - ly__ round your__ ti - ny__ form.
We will serve you all we__ can, Dar - ling, dar - ling__ lit - tle__ man.

Translation of the Czech carol, 'Hajej, nynjej'. This carol may well be sung twice.

189

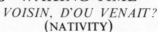

88 WAKING-TIME
VOISIN, D'OU VENAIT?
(NATIVITY)

Pr. Eleanor Farjeon

French
(M.S.)

1. Neigh-bour, what was the sound, I pray, That did a-wake me as I lay, And to their door-ways brought the peo - - ple? Ev - 'ry-one heard it like a chime Peal-ing for joy with be - in a stee - ple: 'Get up, good folk! Get up, good folk, 'tis wa - king - time! Get up, good folk, 'tis wa - king - time!'

2. Nay then, young Mar-tin, know you not That it is this our na - tive spot Sweet Love has cho - sen for his dwell - - ing? In ev-'ry quar - ter ru - mours hum, Ru-mours of news be - yond all tell - ing: 'Wake up, good folk! Wake up, good folk, for Christ is come, Wake up, good folk, for Christ is come.'

3 Neighbours, and is it really true,
 True that the babe so small and new
  Is lying even now among us?
 What can we lay upon his knees—
  He whose arrival angels sung us,
   What can we give,
 What can we give the child to please?

4 Dickon shall bring a ball of silk,
 Peter his son a pot of milk,
  And Tom a sparrow and a linnet,
 Robin a cheese, and Ralph the half
  Part of a cake with cherries in it,
   And jolly Jack,
 And jolly Jack a little calf.

5 I think this child will come to be
 Some sort of workman such as we,
  So he shall have my tools and chattels,
 My well-set saw, my plane, my drill,
  My hammer that so merry rattles,
   And planks of wood,
 And planks of wood to work at will.

6 When we have made our offerings,
 Saying to him the little things
  Whereof all babies born are witting,
 Then we will take our leave and go,
  Bidding goodnight in manner fitting—
   Hush, hush, wee lamb,
 Hush, hush, wee lamb, dream sweetly so.

  7 And in a stable though he lies,
   We in our hearts will soon devise
    Such mansions as can never shame him:
   There we will house and hold him dear,
   And through the world to all proclaim him:
     'Wake up, good folk!
   Wake up, good folk, for Christ is here.'

VOISIN, d'où venait ce grand bruit
Qui m'a réveillé cette nuit
 Et tous les gens du voisinage?
Vraiment, j'étais fort en courroux
 D'entendre partout le village,
  'Sus, sus, bergers!
Sus, sus, bergers réveillez-vous.'

2 Quoi donc, Colin, ne sais-tu pas
 Qu'un Dieu vient de naître ici-bas;
  Qu'il est logé dans une étable?
 Il n'a ni langes ni drapeaux.
  Et dans cet état misérable,
   On ne peut voir
 On ne peut voir rien de plus beau.

3 Qui t'a dit, voisin, qu'en ce lieu
 Voudrait bien s'adresser un Dieu
  Pour qui rien n'est trop magnifique?
 Les anges nous l'ont fait savoir
  Par une charmante musique,
   Qui s'entendit,
 Qui s'entendit hier tout le soir.

4 Sans plus tarder, allons donc tous,
 Allons saluer à genoux
  Notre Seigneur et notre maître:
 Et dans cet aimable séjour,
  Où pour nous l'amour l'a fait naître
   Allons pour lui,
 Allons pour lui mourir d'amour.

5 Partons de suite, cher Colin,
 J'y veux être de bon matin
  Pour lui offrir ma maisonette,
 Où j'ai préparé, sur deux bancs,
  Un lit en forme de couchette,
   Et des linceuls,
 Et des linceuls qui sont tout blancs.

6 Je vais faire tout de mon mieux
 Pour le retenir dans ces lieux,
  Ainsi que Joseph et Marie.
 Quand ils seront tous trois chez-moi
  Ma maison sera plus jolie
   Que le palais,
 Que le palais du plus grand roi.

  7 Dès aujourd'hui, dans ce dessein,
   Sans attendre jusqu'à demain,
    Je veux quitter ma bergerie;
   Et j'abandonne mon troupeau,
   Pour mieux garder toute ma vie,
     Dans ma maison,
   Dans ma maison ce seul agneau.

The tune, with six verses, is in the *Grande Bible des Noëls Angevins*, 1766; there are many variants of the tune, in Anjou and elsewhere, and seven more verses are known of 'Voisin, d'où venait ce grand bruit?' which is here paraphrased.

89 SION'S DAUGHTER
(NATIVITY)

Tr. A.G.

Dutch
(M.S.)

1. O Si - on's daugh - ter, where art thou? Good news have
I to tell_____ thee, A great - er joy I
bring_ thee now Than ev - er yet be - fell_____ thee.

2. A maid - en hath brought forth a son; Great was the
gift she gave_____ us; In Beth - lem was that
life_ be - gun Of him_ who came to save_____ us.

3 As through a casement light will flood
    That darkness may be ended,
So through her maiden motherhood
    The child of God descended.

4 Upon her lap he lay so fair,
    She kissed him and caressed him;
Great was the love she did him bear,
    As to her heart she pressed him.

A translation of the old Netherland carol, 'Waer is die dochter
van Syoen', from *Nederlandsch Volksliederenboek*, by Lange, Riemsdijk, and Kalff, 1896.

90 SONG OF THE SHIP
ES KOMMT EIN SCHIFF
(NATIVITY)

c. 1470, tr. O. B. C.

German, 1608

SOPRANO
ALTO

1. There comes a ship a-sail - ing With an - gels fly - ing
2. This ship is full - y la - den, Right to her high - est

TENOR
BASS

fast; She bears a splen-did car - - go And has a migh-ty mast.
board; She bears the Son from hea - - ven, God's high e - ter - nal Word.

3 Upon the sea unruffled
   The ship moves in to shore,
To bring us all the riches
   She has within her store.

4 And that ship's name is Mary,
   Of flowers the rose is she,
And brings to us her baby
   From sin to set us free.

5 The ship made in this fashion,
   In which such store was cast,
Her sail is Love's sweet passion,
   The Holy Ghost her mast.

Es kommt ein Schiff geladen
   Bis an sein'n höchsten Bord,
Trägt Gottes Sohn voll Gnaden,
   Des Vaters ewig's Wort.

2 Das Schiff geht still im Triebe,
   Es trägt ein teure Last,
Das Segel ist die Liebe
   Der Heilig Geist der Mast.

3 Der Anker haft auf Erden,
   Und das Schiff ist am Land,
Gott's Wort tut uns Fleisch werden,
   Der Sohn ist uns gesandt.

4 Zu Bethlehem geboren
   Im Stall ein Kindelein,
Gibt sich für uns verloren,
   Gelobet muss es sein.

The oldest text, in four stanzas (1 and 2 forming one stanza), is in a MS. 1470-80 (Royal Library, Berlin). Sudermann (*Gesänge*, 1626) gives what has become the better known text, and says that it was found among Tauler's writings. The melody is from the version ('Uns kompt ein Schiff gefahren') in the *Andernach Gesangbuch*, 1608. There is much doubt about Tauler's writings; and Sudermann seems to have rewritten the hymns in his collection. The last lines of the 1470 version are: Der segel is die minne, | Der heilig geist der mast.

91 IN THE TOWN
NOUS VOICI DANS LA VILLE
(NATIVITY)

Pr. Eleanor Farjeon

French, 15th century
(M.S.)

In moderate time

SOPRANO
ALTO

(Joseph)
1. Take heart, the jour-ney's end-ed: I see the twink-ling
2. And how then shall we praise him? A-las, my heart is

TENOR
BASS

lights, Where we shall be be-friend-ed On this the night of
sore That we no gifts can raise him Who are so ve-ry

nights. Now praise the Lord that led us So safe un-to the
poor. We have as much as an-y That on the earth do

(Mary)

town,— Where men will feed and bed us, And I can lay me down.
live,— Al-though we have no pen-ny We have our-selves to give.

Joseph: 3 Look yonder, wife, look yonder!
　　　　　An hostelry I see,
　　　　　Where travellers that wander
　　　　　Will very welcome be.

Mary:　　The house is tall and stately,
　　　　　The door stands open thus;
　　　　　Yet, husband, I fear greatly
　　　　　That inn is not for us.

Joseph: 4 God save you, gentle master!
　　　　　Your littlest room indeed
　　　　　With plainest walls of plaster
　　　　　Tonight will serve our need.

Host:　　For lordings and for ladies
　　　　　I've lodging and to spare;
　　　　　For you and yonder maid is
　　　　　No closet anywhere.

Joseph: 5 Take heart, take heart, sweet Mary,
　　　　　Another inn I spy,
　　　　　Whose host will not be chary
　　　　　To let us easy lie.

Mary:　　Oh, aid me, I am ailing,
　　　　　My strength is nearly gone;
　　　　　I feel my limbs are failing,
　　　　　And yet we must go on.

Joseph: 6 God save you, Hostess, kindly!
　　　　　I pray you, house my wife,
　　　　　Who bears beside me blindly
　　　　　The burden of her life.

Hostess:　My guests are rich men's daughters
　　　　　And sons, I'd have you know!
　　　　　Seek out the poorer quarters
　　　　　Where ragged people go.

Joseph: 7 Good sir, my wife's in labour,
　　　　　Some corner let us keep.

Host:　　Not I: knock up my neighbour,
　　　　　And as for me, I'll sleep.

Mary:　　In all the lighted city
　　　　　Where rich men welcome win,
　　　　　Will not one house for pity
　　　　　Take two poor strangers in?

Joseph: 8 Good woman, I implore you
　　　　　Afford my wife a bed.

Hostess:　Nay, nay, I've nothing for you
　　　　　Except the cattle-shed.

Mary:　　Then gladly in the manger
　　　　　Our bodies we will house,
　　　　　Since men tonight are stranger
　　　　　Than asses are and cows.

Joseph: 9 Take heart, take heart, sweet Mary,
　　　　　The cattle are our friends:
　　　　　Lie down, lie down, sweet Mary,
　　　　　For here the journey ends.

Mary:　　Now praise the Lord that found me
　　　　　This shelter in the town,
　　　　　Where I with friends around me
　　　　　May lay my burden down.

For French words see overleaf.

A paraphrase of the touching old dialogue carol, 'Nous voici dans la ville'. The lovely tune is famous and widespread in France; the words set to it by Lucas Le Moigne ('Or, nous dites Marie') date it as at least not later than *c.* 1450, and the macaronic carol 'Célébrons la naissance' (which is given to the tune together with 'Nous voici' in the *Grande Bible des Noëls* of 1766) is clearly a fifteenth-century work. Other words (not all religious) have been sung to it, e.g. 'Hélas! je l'ai perdue', 'Voulez-vous plaire aux dames', 'Bergère que j'adore', and 'Chantons, je vous en prie'. In 1676 Le Bègue used the melody for an organ prelude; and its strains upon the organ are often heard creeping into the silence of the consecration at Christmas time in French churches.

We have arranged it in parts; and it can be sung thus in church, or else as a little play upon the stage.

Dr. Neale's words 'A day, a day of glory' are set to this tune in *The Cowley Carol Book.*

Joseph: Nous voici dans la ville
Où naquit autrefois
Le roi le plus habile
Et le plus saint des rois.

Marie: Elevons la pensée
Vers le Dieu qui conduit
Nos pas cette journée,
Voici venir la nuit.

Joseph: 2 Quelle reconnaissance
Pouvons-nous rendre à Dieu?
De la sainte assistance
Qu'il nous donne en tout lieu?

Marie: Offrons nos corps, nos âmes
A notre créateur,
Allumons donc la flamme
De l'amour dans nos coeurs.

Joseph: 3 Allons, chère Marie,
De vers cet horloger.
C'est une hôtellerie;
Nous y pourrons loger.
Mon cher Monsieur, de grâce,
N'ayez vous point chez vous
Quelque petite place—
Quelque chambre pour nous?

L'Hôte: 4 Vous perdez votre peine
Vous venez un peu tard;
Ma maison est trop pleine,
Allez voir autre part.

Joseph: Passons à l'autre rue,
Laquelle est vis-à-vis
Tout devant notre rue,
Je vois d'autres logis.

Marie: 5 Joseph, ton bras, de grâce,
Je ne puis plus marcher
Je me trouve si lasse.
Il faut pourtant chercher.

Joseph: Patron des trois couronnes
Avez-vous logement
Chez vous, pour deux personnes?
Quelque trou seulement!

L'Hôte: 6 J'ai noble compagnie
Dont j'aurai du profit.
Je hais la gueuserie—
C'est tout dire, il suffit!

Marie: Salut, ma chère hôtesse,
Ayez pitié de nous.
Sensible à ma détresse,
Recevez-nous chez vous.

Joseph: 7 En attendant, madame,
Que j'ai un logement,
Permettez que ma femme
Se repose un moment.

L'Hôtesse: Très volontiers, m'amie,
Mettez-vous sur le banc.
Monsieur, voyez la Pie
Ou bien le Cheval Blanc.

8 Dans l'état déplorable
Où Joseph est réduit,
Il découvre une étable
Malgré la sombre nuit.
C'est la seule retraite
Qui reste à son espoir
Ainsi que le prophète
Avait su le prévoir.

92 PUER NOBIS
(NATIVITY)

15th century
Tr. O.B.C.

Piae Cantiones, 1582
(Geoffrey Shaw)

(VOICES IN UNISON)

FULL

ORGAN

Ped.

1. Un - to us a boy is born! King of all cre - a - tion, Came he to a world for - lorn, The Lord of ev - 'ry na - - - - - - - - - - - tion.

1. Pu - er no - bis nas - ci - tur Rec - tor an - ge - lo - rum, In hoc mun - do pas - ci - tur Do - mi - nus Do - mi - no - - - - - - - - rum.

SOPRANOS

2. Cra - dled in a stall was he With sleep - y cows and
2. *In prae - se - pe po - ni - tur Sub foe - no a - si -*

Senza Ped.

ass - es; But the ve - ry beasts could see That
- no - rum. Cog - no - ve - runt Do - mi - num Chris -

he all men sur - pass - - - - - - - es.
-tum re - gem coe - lo - - - - - - - rum.

198

TENORS AND BASSES

3. He - rod then with fear was filled: 'A prince', he said, 'in
3. *Hinc He - ro - des ti - mu - it___ Mag - no cum do -*

Ped.

Jew - - ry!' All the lit - tle boys he killed At
-lo - - re, Et pu - e - ros oc - ci - dit, in -

Beth - lem in his fu - - - - - - - - ry.
-fan - tes cum li - vo - - - - - - - re.

199

SOPRANOS

4. Now may Ma - ry's son, who came So long a - go to
4. *Qui na - tus de vir - gi - ne___ Di - e ho - di -*

Ch.

Gt.

love us, Lead us all with hearts a - flame Un -
- er - na Du - cat nos cum gra - ti - a Ad

-to the joys a - bove_____us.
gau - di - a su - per - - - - - - - - - na.

The words and original melody of 'Puer nobis nascitur' are in a Trier MS. of the fifteenth century. There are many variants, given in Zahn, Dreves, and Baümker; a German translation ('Uns ist geboren ein Kindelein') is printed by Spangenberg, 1544, in the Mainz *Cantual*, 1605, and elsewhere. The melody in this form is in *Piae Cantiones*, 1582 (see note to No. 141), and the words are from the version of Mone (*Lateinische Hymnen*), who prints the Trier form.

93 MARY'S WANDERING
MARIAS WANDERSCHAFT
(THE PASSION)

Tr. A.F. D.

German
(M.S.)

Rather slowly

SOPRANO
ALTO

1. Once Ma - ry would go_wan-der-ing, To all the_lands would run,
2. Whom met she as she jour-neyed forth? Saint Pe - ter,_that good man,

TENOR
BASS

That she might find_ her_ son, that she_ might_ find her son.
Who sad - ly did_ her_ scan, who sad - ly____ did her scan.

FA - BURDEN to verses 4 & 7

S.
A.

4. 'Too well, too well, I've seen thy son; 'Twas by a pal - ace - gate,
7. 'Nay, Ma - ry, cease thy weep-ing, dear: The wounds they are but small;

T.
B.

Most griev - - ous was_ his_ state.'_____
But heav'n is won_ for_ all!'_____

Most griev - ous was_ his_ state.'
But heav'n is won_ for_ all!'

Most griev - ous was his state, most griev - ous_ was his state.'
But heav'n is won_ for_ all, but heav'n is____ won for all!'

Most griev - ous was his state, most griev - ous was his state.'
But heav'n is won for all, but heav'n is won for all!'

3 'O tell me have you seen him yet—
  The one I love the most—
  The son whom I have lost?'

4 'Too well, too well, I've seen thy son;
  'Twas by a palace-gate,
  Most grievous was his state.'

5 'O say, what wore he on his head?'
  'A crown of thorns he wore;
  A cross he also bore.'

6 'Ah me! and he must bear that cross,
  Till he's brought to the hill,
  For cruel men to kill.'

7 'Nay, Mary, cease thy weeping, dear:
  The wounds they are but small;
  But heaven is won for all!'

MARIA die wollt' wandern geh'n,
Wollt' alle Land ausgeh'n,
Wollt' suchen ihren Sohn.

2 Was begegnet ihr auf der Reise?
  Sankt Petrus der heil'ge Mann,
  Ganz traurig schaut s'ihn an.

3 'Habt ihr denn nicht gesehen
  Mein allerliebsten Sohn,
  Den ich verloren han?'

4 'Wohl hab' ich ihn gesehen
  Vor einem Judenhaus;
  Ganz traurig sah er aus.'

5 'Was trug er auf seinem Haupte?'
  'Von Dornen eine Kron',
  Das Kreuz, das trug er schon.'

6 'Das Kreuz, das musst' er tragen
  Bis an dieselbige Stadt
  Da er gemartert ward.'

7 'Maria, lass das Weinen;
  Die Wunden, die sind klein,
  Das Himmelreich ist mein!'

'Marias Wanderschaft' ('Maria die wollt' wandern geh'n') is one version of this legend, and to it belongs this folk-melody, which was published by Friedlaender. The third line of each verse is repeated.
  See No. 179 for Brahms's tune to another version of the ballad.

94 EASTER EGGS

Tr. A.F.D.

Russian
(M.S.)

Eas - ter eggs! Eas - ter eggs! Give to him that_ begs!
Those who hoard can't aff-ord— moth and rust their re-ward!
Eas - ter - tide, like a bride, comes, and won't be de-nied.

Christ the Lord is a - ris - en,— is a - ris - en. To the
Those who

'm_____ For

poor, o - pen door, some-thing give from your store! For
love free - ly give— long and well may they live!

Christ the Lord is a - ris - en,— is a - ris - en.

Words and melody from the traditional Easter song, 'Dalalin,
Dalalin, po Yaichenku', in Rimsky-Korsakov's *Russian National Songs*, 1877.

95 NOW GLAD OF HEART
WIR WOLLEN ALLE FRÖHLICH SEIN
(EASTER: ASCENSION: TRINITY SUNDAY)

Tr. A.H. Fox-Strangways

German, 16th century
(Geoffrey Shaw)

1. Now glad of heart be ev - 'ry one! The fight is fought, the
2. Who on the rood was cru - ci - fied, Who rose a - gain,— as

day— is won, The Christ— is set up - on his throne,
at— this tide, In glo - - ry to his Fa - ther's side,

3 Who baffled death and harrowed hell
And led the souls that loved him well
All in the light of lights to dwell;

4 To him we lift our heart and voice
And in his paradise rejoice
With harp and pipe and happy noise.

5 Then rise, all Christian folk, with me
And carol forth the One in Three
That was, and is, and is to be,

6 By faith, the shield of heart and mind,
Through love, which suffers and is kind,
In hope, that rides upon the wind.

WIR wollen alle fröhlich sein
In dieser osterlichen Zeit
Denn unser Heil an Gotte leit.

2 Es ist erstanden Jesu Christ
Der an dem Kreuz gestorben ist
Dem sei Lob, Ehr' zu aller Frist.

3 Er hat zerstört der Hellen Pfort
Und all die seinen herausgeführt
Und uns erlöst vom ewigen Tod.

4 Wir singen all Lob, Ehr' und Preis
Dem einigen Gottes Sohne weiss
Der uns erkauft das Paradeis.

5 Es freu' sich all die Christenheit
Und lob' die heilige Dreifaltigkeit
Von nun an bis in Ewigkeit.

In some versions of 'Wir wollen alle fröhlich sein', one or more stanzas of *Alleluya* (repeated) are
added. This was 'an old song' already in Spangenberg's *Christlichs Gesangbüchlein*, 1568. It is also in
the *Gesangbuch der Brüder in Behemen*, Nürnberg, 1544, and elsewhere.

96 HILARITER
(EASTER: SPRING: SUMMER)

Tr. O.B.C.

German, 1623
(M.S.)

Rather quickly

SOPRANO
ALTO

1. The whole bright world re - joi - ces now, *Hi - la - ri -*
2. Then shout be - neath the rac - ing skies,

TENOR
BASS

-ter, hi - la - ri - ter; The birds do sing on
To him who rose that

ev - 'ry bough *Al - le - lu - ya, al - le - lu - ya.*
we might rise,

3 And all you living things make praise,
    Hilariter, hilariter;
He guideth you on all your ways,
    Alleluya, alleluya.

4 He, Father, Son, and Holy Ghost—
    Hilariter, hilariter!—
Our God most high, our joy and boast.
    Alleluya, alleluya.

DIE ganze Welt, Herr Jesu Christ,
Hilariter, hilariter,
In deiner Orstend fröhlich ist,
Alleluya, alleluya.

2 Das himmlisch Heer in Himmel singt
Hilariter, hilariter,
Die Christenheit auf Erden klingt,
Alleluya, alleluya.

3 Jetzt grünet was nur grünen kann
Hilariter, hilariter,
Die Baüm' zu blühen fangen an.
Alleluya, alleluya.

4 Es singen jetzt die Vögel all,
Hilariter, hilariter,
Jetzt singt und klingt die Nachtigall
Alleluya, alleluya.

5 Der Sonnenschein jetzt kommt herein
Hilariter, hilariter,
Und gibt der Welt ein neuen Schein.
Alleluya, alleluya.

The earliest appearance of 'Die ganze Welt' is in the Cologne *Kirchengesäng*, 1623;
it appears later in several other books, e.g. at Mainz, 1628, Prague, 1655, and Strassburg, 1697.

97 THE SECRET FLOWER

GEBOR'N IST UNS EIN KINDELEIN

(EASTER: WHITSUNTIDE: SAINTS' DAYS)

German, 17th century
Pr. Eleanor Farjeon

German, 16th century
(M.S.)

1. This child was born to men of God:
   Love to the world was giv - en; In him were truth and beau - ty met, On him was set At birth the seal of hea - ven.

2. He came the Word to man - i - fest,
   Earth to the stars he rais - es: The teach - er's err - ors are not his, The Truth he is: No man can speak his prais - es.

3 He evil fought and overcame,
He took from death the power;
To all that follow where he goes
At last he shows
The kingdom's secret flower.

4 The secret flower shall bloom on earth
In them that have beholden;
The heavenly spirit shall be plain
In them again,
As first it was of olden.

5 The spirit like a light shall shine,
Evil himself dispelling,
The spirit like a wind shall blow,
And death shall go
Unfeared in her own dwelling.

6 And by the spirit shall be known
Heroes and saints and sages;
Yea, they shall walk in all men's sight,
Amid the light
God sent to crown the ages.

GEBOR'N ist uns ein Kindelein
Von einer Jungfrau reine
Gott Vater Sohn und heil'ger Geist
Die sind gereist
Mit Maria alleine.

2 Wir woll'n Gott loben in Ewigkeit
Darzu das Kindelein klein
Und Mariam die Mutter sein
Die Jungfrau fein
Woll uns ihr Gnad' mitteilen.

3 Freu dich Maria in Ewigkeit!
Darum du hast empfangen
Den Spiegel der Dreifaltigkeit
Dein Lob ist bereit;
Zu dir haben wir Verlangen.

4 Das Kindlein ist der Gnaden voll;
Es gibt uns gute Lehre.
Sein Lob niemand aussprechen kann;
Ist sonder wann
Wir danken ihm seiner Lehre.

5 Er hat gelitten den bittern Tod
Für unser Sünden alle;
Und gibt den Sündern guten Trost,
Hat uns erlost
Wohl von dem ewigen Fall.

6 O Herz halt uns in deiner Hut
Das wir nicht mögen sterben
In unser Sünd und Missetat,
O ewiger Gott
Dein' Gnad' hilf uns erwerben.

A paraphrase of 'Gebor'n ist uns ein Kindelein'. Melody in the Mainz *Cantual*, 1605, but certainly of the sixteenth century, and perhaps earlier, says Riemann. Words and melody in the Cologne *Gesangbuch*, 1634.

98 SPRING HAS COME
(SPRING)

Piae Cantiones, 1582
Tr. Steuart Wilson

Ibid.
(G.S.)

1. Now— the spring— has come— a - gain,—
Cold— and wet— are quite— for - got,—

joy— and warmth will fol - - low;—
north - ward flies— the

1st time ... *2nd time*

swal - - low;

Ov - er sea— and land— and air— spring's soft touch— is
All our sin - ews feel— new strung,— hearts are light— that

ev - 'ry - where— And— the world— looks clean - - er;
once— were wrung,— Youth - ful zests— are keen - - er.

2 All the woods are new in leaf, all the fruit is budding,
   Bees are humming round the hive, done with winter's
      brooding;
   Seas are calm and blue again, clouds no more foretell
      the rain,
         Winds are soft and tender;
   High above, the kingly sun laughs once more his
      course to run,
         Shines in all his splendour.

3 God is in the midst of her, God commands her duty;
   Earth does but reflect his light, mirrors back his beauty;
   God's the fount whence all things flow, great and
      small, above, below,
         God's their only maker:
   We but poorest patterns are of that mind beyond
      compare,
         God our great creator.

Neale turned this Spring carol, 'In vernali tempore', from *Piae Cantiones*, 1582 (see note to No. 141), into a Christmas carol in 1853 ('O'er the hill and o'er the vale'), as he did also with No. 99.

99 FLOWER CAROL
(SPRING)

Piae Cantiones, 1582
Tr. O. B. C.

Ibid.
(M. S.)

This harmonization may be used throughout if preferred

SOPRANO
ALTO

TENOR
BASS

1. Spring has now un-wrapped the flowers, Day is fast re - viv - ing,

Life in all her grow - ing powers Towards the light is striv - ing:

Gone the i - ron touch of cold, Win - ter time and frost time,

Seed-lings, work-ing through the mould, Now make up for lost____ time.

2 Herb and plant that, winter long,
    Slumbered at their leisure,
Now bestirring, green and strong,
    Find in growth their pleasure:
All the world with beauty fills,
    Gold the green enhancing;
Flowers make glee among the hills,
    And set the meadows dancing.

3 Through each wonder of fair days
    God himself expresses;
Beauty follows all his ways,
    As the world he blesses:
So, as he renews the earth,
    Artist without rival,
In his grace of glad new birth
    We must seek revival.

4 Earth puts on her dress of glee;
    Flowers and grasses hide her;
We go forth in charity—
    Brothers all beside her;
For, as man this glory sees
    In the awakening season,
Reason learns the heart's decrees,
    And hearts are led by reason.

5 Praise the Maker, all ye saints;
    He with glory girt you,
He who skies and meadows paints
    Fashioned all your virtue;
Praise him, seers, heroes, kings,
    Heralds of perfection;
Brothers, praise him, for he brings
    All to resurrection!

FA-BURDEN for verses 2 and 4 (melody in the tenor)

2. Herb and plant that, win-ter long, Slum-bered at their leis-ure,
4. Earth puts on her dress of glee; Flowers and grass-es hide her;

Now be-stirr-ing, green and strong, Find in growth their pleas-ure:
We go forth in cha-ri-ty— Bro-thers all be-side her;

All the world with beau - ty fills, Gold the green en-
For, as man this glo - ry sees In the a-wak'n - ing

-hanc - - ing; Flowers make glee a - mong the hills, And
sea - - son, Rea - son learns the heart's de - crees, And

set the mea - dows danc - - - - - - - - - - - ing.
hearts are led by rea - - - - - - - - - - son.

set the mea - dows danc - - - - ing.
hearts are led by rea - - - - son.

danc - - - - - - - - - ing.
rea - - - - - - - - son.

Verses 3 and 5

3. Thro' each won - der of fair days God him-self ex - press - es;
5. Praise the Mak - er, all ye saints; He with glo - ry girt you,

S.
A.

3. Thro' each won-der of fair days__ God him-self ex - press-
5. Praise the Mak - er, all ye saints;__ He with glo - ry girt__

3. Thro' each won- der of fair days God him-self ex - press - es;
5. Praise the Mak - er, all ye saints; He with glo - ry girt you,

T.
B.

Beau-ty fol-lows all his ways, As the world he bless - es:
He who skies and mea-dows paints Fash-ion'd all your vir - - tue;

- es; Beau-ty fol-lows all his ways,_ As the world he bless-es:
you, He who skies and mea-dows paints_ Fash-ion'd all your vir-tue;

Beau-ty fol-lows all his ways, As the world he bless - es:
He who skies and mea-dows paints Fash-ion'd all your vir - - tue;

So, as he re-news the earth, Art-ist with-out ri - val, In his grace of
Praise him, se-ers, he-roes, kings, Her-alds of per-fec - tion; Bro-thers, praise him,

So, as he re-news_ the earth,_ In his
Praise him, se-ers, he - roes, kings,_ Bro-thers,

Art- ist with-out ri - val, In his grace of
Her-alds of per- fec - tion; Bro-thers, praise him,

So, as he__ re - news_ the__ earth,__ In his grace of
Praise him, se - ers, he-roes, Her-alds of per-fec - tion; Bro-thers, praise him,

glad new birth We must seek re - vi - - - - val.
for he brings All to re-sur-rec - - - - tion!

grace of glad new birth We must seek_ re - vi - val.
praise him, for he brings All to re - - sur - - rec - tion!

glad new birth We must seek re - vi - - - - val.
for he brings All to re-sur-rec - - - - tion!

glad__ new__ birth___ We must seek re - vi - val.
for__ he __ brings___ All to re-sur-rec - tion!

This is a free translation, with a doxology, of the words proper to the melody of No. 136, 'Tempus adest floridum', the Spring carol which Neale turned into a Christmas carol by writing his render-ing of the legend of 'Good King Wenceslas'. We have therefore reprinted the proper tune here, with the suggestion that it should be sung as a Spring carol.

100 THE MESSAGE
(GENERAL)

Pr. E. B. G.

Dutch
(M.S.)

1. A mes - sage came to a mai - den young; The
   an - gel stood be - side her, In shi - ning robes and with gold - en tongue, He
   told what should be - tide her: The maid was lost in won - der Her world was

2. No great - er news could a mes - sen - ger bring; For
   'twas from that young mo - ther He came, who walked on the earth as a king, And
   yet was all men's bro - ther: His truth has spread like leav - en, 'Twill mar - ry

(Tenors) In shi - ning He came, who walked

In shi - ning robes and with gold - en tongue, He
on the earth as a king, And

216

rent ___ a - sun - - der— Ah! how___ could___ she Christ's mo - ther
earth ___ to heav - - en, Till all___ a - - gree In cha - ri -

By God's most high _____ de - cree!
To dwell from sea _____ to sea.

be
- ty   (Tenors) By God's most high   de - cree!
       To dwell from sea   to sea.

By God's most high   de - - cree!
To dwell from sea   to   sea.

3 He came, God's Word to the world here below;
   And round him there did gather
  A band who found that this teacher to know
  Was e'en to know the Father:
     He healed the sick who sought him,
     Forgave the foes who fought him;
      Beside the sea
      Of Galilee
      He set the nations free.

4 And sometimes trumpets from Sion ring out,
   And tramping comes, and drumming—
  'Thy kingdom come,' so we cry; and they shout,
  'It comes!' and still 'tis coming—
     Far, far ahead, to win us,
     Yet with us, nay within us;
      Till all shall see
      That King is he,
      The Love from Galilee!

Melody and words of 'De Boodschap van Maria' (Er was een maagdetje)
which is freely translated in the first verse. From the *Nederlandsch Volksliederenboek*, 1896.

101 GEMS OF DAY

LE VERMEIL DU SOLEIL
(GENERAL)

N. Denisot
Pr. Patrick R. Chalmers

French, 1553
(M.S.)

1. All the gay gems of day— Pearls the morn-ing sky a-dorn-ing,
Man-i-fold gems of gold, Gold-en get-ting now day's set-ting,

Are the sun's pret-ty ones Of his shi-ning or de-cli-ning,

Are his joys, birth-day toys—These God's ve-ry babe make mer - - ry;

2 When Sir Sun his course done,
   Westward stooping home's gone drooping,
   It is naught, look! new wrought
   Joy and beauty bear his duty—
    Planets peep down night's deep,
   Softly seeming gold and dreaming
    Jasmine o'er heaven's door,
   Lest God's only babe fall lonely.

3 Newly-born King of morn,
   Noon and night time, dark and light time,
   Be our light, day and night,
   Ne'er withholden, greatlier golden
    Than the boon sun at noon,
   Than the garland sheen of starland;
    Saviour small, light us all—
   Light our blindness, of thy kindness!

LE vermeil du soleil
Quand l'aurore nous redore
Tous les cieux radieux
Ou quand même en l'extrême
De son jour fait séjour
Près la tente de sa tante
Chéant bas ne veut pas
Que sa roue plus on loue.

2 C'est bien peu que son feu
Aille arrière sa lumière
En égard au regard
De la voie qui flamboie
Cette nuit à minuit
Sous l'étoile qui au voile
Sombre et noir fait devoir
A son maître qui vient naître.

3 Mais oyez et voyez
La naissance l'Excellence
De la nuit qui nous luit
Précieuse, bienheureuse,
Nuit des nuits, nos ennuis
Dieu déchasse, Dieu nous trace
Ses saints pas, Dieu met bas
Toute outrance et puissance.

Paraphrased from 'Le vermeil du soleil', *Cantiques du Premier Advénement de Jésus-Christ*, par Le
Comte d'Alsinois (Nicholas Denisot), Paris, 1553. There are twenty verses in the original; nine of
them will be found in *A Book of Old Carols*, by H. J. L. J. Massé and Charles Kennedy Scott, 1907,
No. 15, p. 24. The melody is stated to be by Marc-Antoine Muret in a MS. note, apparently of the
sixteenth century, in the British Museum copy.

102 GABRIEL'S MESSAGE
(GENERAL: EASTER)

Piae Cantiones, 1582
Tr. J. M. Neale

Ibid.
(G. S.)

1. Ga-briel's mes-sage does a - way Sa-tan's curse and Sa-tan's sway, Out of
2. He that comes des-pised shall reign; He that can-not die, be slain; Death by

dark-ness brings our Day: *So, be - hold, All the gates of heav'n un - fold.*
death its death shall gain:

3 Weakness shall the strong confound;
  By the hands, in grave-clothes wound,
  Adam's chains shall be unbound:

  So, behold, etc.

4 By the sword that was his own,
  By that sword, and that alone,
  Shall Goliath be o'erthrown:

  So, behold, etc.

5 Art by art shall be assailed;
  To the cross shall Life be nailed;
  From the grave shall Hope be hailed:

  So, behold, etc.

The words, written by Neale in 1853, to this tune have been slightly altered, to bring them more in accordance with the original of 'Angelus emittitur' upon which they were based; the original refrain is 'Igitur Porta coeli panditur' and Neale's refrain runs 'Therefore sing,—Glory to the Infant King'. Two Christmas verses not in the original are omitted. The earliest known version is in *Piae Cantiones*, 1582 (see note to No. 141).

103 THE BIRDS
(GENERAL)

Tr. O.B.C.

Czech
(M.S.)

CHORUS

1. From out of a wood did a cuc - koo fly,   He
2. A pi - geon flew o - ver to Ga - li - lee,   He
3. A dove set - tled down up - on Na - za - reth, SOLI   And

SOPRANO
ALTO

A.T.B. hum

Cuc - koo,
Vrer - croo,
Tsu - croo,

TENOR
BASS

came to a man - ger with joy - ful cry,   He
strut - ted and cooed, and was full of glee,   And
ten - der - ly chant - ed with all his breath SOLI   'O

(hum)

Cuc - koo;
Vrer - croo,
Tsu - croo:

CHORUS

hopped, he curt - - sied, round he flew, And loud his
showed with jew - - elled wings un - furled, His joy that
you,' he cooed, 'so good and true, My beau - ty

(hum)

ju - - bi - la - - tion grew,
Christ was in the world,
do I give to you— SOLI

Cuc - koo, cuc - koo, cuc - koo.
Vrer - croo, vrer - croo, vrer - croo.
Tsu - croo, tsu - croo, tsu - croo'.

A translation of an unpublished carol, 'Zezulka z lesa vylitla, kuku', which was taken down from a Czech peasant girl in the Christmas of 1921 at Policka, in the hills between Bohemia and Moravia, and kindly communicated by Miss Jakubičková.

104 HOW BRIGHTLY BEAMS

WIE SCHÖN LEUCHTET

(GENERAL: EPIPHANY: EASTER)

FIRST VERSION

Nicolai and Schlegel
Tr. C. Winkworth

German (P. Nicolai?)
(harm. J. S. Bach)

1. How bright-ly beams the morn-ing star! What sud-den ra-diance
Bright-ness of God, that breaks our night And fills the dark-ened

from a - far Doth glad us with its shi - ning?
souls with light Who long for truth were pi - ning!

Thy word, Je - sus, in - ly feeds us, Right-ly leads us,

Life be - stow - ing. Praise, oh praise such love o'er - flow - ing!
Life be-stow - - ing.

2 Through thee alone can we be blest;
  Then deep be on our hearts imprest
    The love that thou hast borne us;
  So make us ready to fulfil
  With burning zeal thy holy will,
    Though men may vex or scorn us;
  Saviour, let us never lose thee,
        For we choose thee,
        Thirst to know thee;
  All we are and have we owe thee!

3 O praise to him who came to save,
  Who conquer'd death and burst the
      grave;
    Each day new praise resoundeth
  To him the Lamb who once was slain,
  The friend whom none shall trust in vain,
    Whose grace for ay aboundeth;
  Sing, ye heavens, tell the story
        Of his glory,
        Till his praises
  Flood with light earth's darkest places!

WIE schön leuchtet der Morgenstern
Voll Gnad' und Wahrheit von dem Herrn,
Die süsse Wurzel Jesse!
Du Sohn Davids aus Jacobs Stamm,
Mein König und mein Bräutigam,
Hast mir mein Herz besessen.
Lieblich, freundlich,
  Schön und herrlich,
  Gross und ehrlich,
Reich von Gaben,
Hoch und sehr prächtig erhaben.

2 Geuss sehr tief in mein Herz hinein
O du, mein Herr und Gott allein,
Die Flamme deiner Liebe,
Dass ich beständig in dir bleib'
Und mich kein Unfall von dir treib',
Nichts kränke noch betrübe.
In dir lass mir
  Ohn' Aufhören
  Sich vermehren
Lieb' und Freude,
Dass der Tod uns selbst nicht scheide.

3 Sing unserm Gott recht oft und viel
Und lasst andächtig Saitenspiel
Ganz freudenreich erschallen
Dem allerliebsten Jesulein,
Dem wunderschönen Braütigam mein,
Zu Ehren und Gefallen.
  Singet, springet,
  Jubilieret, triumphieret
Dankt dem Herrn!
Gross ist der König der Ehren.

Three verses of the seven in the recast by J. A. Schlegel (1721-93), 'Wie herrlich strahlt der Morgenstern', of 'Wie schön leuchtet der Morgenstern', which appeared with the tune in Nicolai's *Freudenspiegel*, 1599. The famous tune, to which very soon many city chimes in Germany were set, was published with Nicolai's hymn, and may therefore be by the author and composer of 'Wachet auf'. It may in part have been suggested by earlier melodies, especially by 'Resonet in Laudibus' (No. 77). The translation is almost entirely that of Miss C. Winkworth, 1863. See No. 193, where this tune is used as accompaniment to Cornelius's song 'The Kings'.

104 HOW BRIGHTLY BEAMS
WIE SCHÖN LEUCHTET
(GENERAL : EPIPHANY : EASTER)
SECOND VERSION

Nicolai and Schlegel
Tr. C. Winkworth

German (P. Nicolai?)
(harm. F. Mendelssohn-Bartholdy)

1. How bright-ly beams the morn-ing star! What sud-den ra-diance
Bright-ness of God, that breaks our night And fills the dark-ened

from a - far Doth glad us with its shi - - ning?
souls with light Who long for truth were pi - - ning!

Thy word, Je - sus, in - ly feeds us, Right-ly leads us,

Life be - stow - ing. Praise, oh praise such love o'er - flow - - ing!

2 Through thee alone can we be blest;
Then deep be on our hearts imprest
  The love that thou hast borne us;
So make us ready to fulfil
With burning zeal thy holy will,
  Though men may vex or scorn us;
Saviour, let us never lose thee,
    For we choose thee,
    Thirst to know thee;
All we are and have we owe thee!

3 O praise to him who came to save,
Who conquer'd death and burst the
    grave;
  Each day new praise resoundeth
To him the Lamb who once was slain,
The friend whom none shall trust in vain,
  Whose grace for ay aboundeth;
Sing, ye heavens, tell the story
    Of his glory,
    Till his praises
Flood with light earth's darkest places!

WIE schön leuchtet der Morgenstern
Voll Gnad' und Wahrheit von dem Herrn,
  Die süsse Wurzel Jesse!
Du Sohn Davids aus Jacobs Stamm,
Mein König und mein Bräutigam,
  Hast mir mein Herz besessen.
Lieblich, freundlich,
    Schön und herrlich,
    Gross und ehrlich,
Reich von Gaben,
Hoch und sehr prächtig erhaben.

2 Geuss sehr tief in mein Herz hinein
O du, mein Herr und Gott allein,
  Die Flamme deiner Liebe,
Dass ich beständig in dir bleib'
Und mich kein Unfall von dir treib',
  Nichts kränke noch betrübe.
In dir lass mir
    Ohn' Aufhören
    Sich vermehren
Lieb' und Freude,
Dass der Tod uns selbst nicht scheide.

3 Sing unserm Gott recht oft und viel
Und lasst andächtig Saitenspiel
  Ganz freudenreich erschallen
Dem allerliebsten Jesulein,
Dem wunderschönen Braütigam mein,
  Zu Ehren und Gefallen.
    Singet, springet,
    Jubilieret, triumphieret
Dankt dem Herrn!
Gross ist der König der Ehren.

Three verses of the seven in the recast by J. A. Schlegel (1721-93), 'Wie herrlich strahlt der Morgenstern', of 'Wie schön leuchtet der Morgenstern', which appeared with the tune in Nicolai's *Freudenspiegel*, 1599. The famous tune, to which very soon many city chimes in Germany were set, was published with Nicolai's hymn, and may therefore be by the author and composer of 'Wachet auf'. It may in part have been suggested by earlier melodies, especially by 'Resonet in Laudibus' (No. 77). The translation is almost entirely that of Miss C. Winkworth, 1863. See No. 193, where this tune is used as accompaniment to Cornelius's song 'The Kings'.

105 THE GARDEN OF JESUS
(GENERAL)

Tr. E. B. G.

Dutch, 1633
(Geoffrey Shaw)

3 The rose's name is Patience, pruned to greater might;
   The marigold's, Obedience, plentiful and bright:
   There angels sing etc.

4 And Hope and Faith are there; but of these three the best
   Is Love, whose crown-imperial spreads o'er all the rest:
   There angels sing etc.

5 And one thing fairest is in all that lovely maze,
   The gardener, Jesus Christ, whom all the flowers praise:
   There angels sing etc.

6 O Jesus, all my good and all my bliss! Ah me!
   Thy garden make my heart, which ready is for thee!
   There angels sing etc.

The Dutch words and melody of 'Jesus' Bloemhof' (beginning 'Heer Jesus heeft een hofken waart vol bloemen staat') occur in *Geestlijke Harmonie* (1633), and were reprinted in *Oude en Nieuwere Kerst-Liederen* (1852). A translation ('Our Master hath a garden') by S. S. Greatheed was printed in *The Ecclesiologist* for February, 1856, and was included by E. Sedding in *Antient Christmas Carols*, 1860, and in *The People's Hymnal*, 1867. It does not, however, quite fit the melody; and therefore, while we have preserved the 'gentle, soothing' flutes, we give a new translation here.

226

106 SO, BROTHER
FESANS RAIJOUISSANCE
(GENERAL)

Père Christin Prost
Pr. A. A. Milne

Besançon
(M. S.)

Moderately quick

SOPRANO
ALTO

1. Now, bro-thers, lift your voi-ces, And laugh and dance and sing,— For
2. Poor Sa-tan, you can hear him, Is ra-ging down in hell,— For
3. And fierc-er now and fast-er The flames come roar-ing in — On

TENOR
BASS

all the world re-joi-ces That Christ the Lord is King.— With
now there's none to fear him, And none to wish him well.— The
him that was their mas-ter, On Sa-tan, prince of sin.— Then,

joy in him to arm you The de-vil can not harm you: So,
fires that he was keep-ing Are on his foot-steps creep-ing: So,
bro-ther, as he lies there, Then, bro-ther, as he dies there, Come

bro-ther! laugh and sing,
bro-ther! laugh and sing That Christ the Lord is King.—
laugh and dance and sing—

A paraphrase of three verses (out of twelve) in the original carol 'Fesans raijouissance' (see overleaf)
written by Père Christin Prost, a Capuchin friar who died in 1676. His carols were reprinted in
Recueil de Noëls anciens au patois de Besançon, edited by Th. Belamy, 1842. The old air on which the
carol was written was known as 'Je suis dans la tristesse' or 'De turlu turlutu'.

227

FESANS raijouissance,
　　Risans, dansans, chantans
Ca voicy ne naissance
　　Que tout le monde aitend.
In Prince ot né su tare
Que vint finir lai gare
　　Et tur-lu, tur-lu-tu
　　Tout perissa sans lu.

2 Lou Diable peste, enraige
　　D'être dedans l'Enfa;
Lou droule ouzé en caige,
　　Que lou peut Lucifa,
Qu'ot dedans ne chandére
D'huile ou d'autre maitére
　　Et tur-lu, tur-lu-tu
　　Y n'en soëthiret pu.

3 Pourquoi donc, peute béte,
　　Ai-te tanta Adam?
Qu'aivouë-te dans lai téte,
　　Dit, malheureux Satan?
Te nous crayon tous pâdre;
Main voici lou grand Matre
　　Et tur-lu, tur-lu-tu
　　Qu'ot pou nous daicendu.

107 PRAISE TO GOD
(GENERAL)

Tr. A. F. D.

Russian
(M. S.)

Moderato e maestoso

Praise to God in the high - est! Bless us, O
May the truth in its beau - ty flou - rish tri be
May the good be o - beyed, and e - vil be
Peace on earth, and good - will, — be ev - er a -

Fa - ther!
- um - phant:
con - quered:
- mongst us:

Fine

Praise to thee.

(S.A.) Praise to God in the

(T.B.) Guide and pros - per the
May the mills bring us
Give us laugh - ter, and

Melody in tenor

Fine

high - - est! to God, *Praise to thee.*

na - tions, ru - lers and peo - ple:
bread,— for food and for giv - ing;
set — us gai - ly re - joic - ing:

Praise to — thee.

'Slava Bogu na nebye' was printed by Yakushkin in 1815, and exists in many variants, as well as in Rimsky-Korsakov, who calls it a Christmas Song, though its many verses, from which we have selected, are all of general national application. The melody was used by Beethoven in his Quartet, Op. 59, No. 2; by Rimsky-Korsakov in his cantata 'Slava'; and by Mussorgsky in the Coronation Scene of 'Boris Godunov'.

108 THE KINGDOM

QUOI, MA VOISINE?

(GENERAL)

François Colletet (1675)
Pr. Patrick R. Chalmers

Angevin
(M.S.)

Rather quickly

1. 'O, I have seen a king's new ba - by,' Su - san she said,
2. 'O the king's son / he lies so spare - ly,' Su - san she told,

'Joy up-on his bright, dear birth - day be And on his bright head!'
'No lace to lap - pen him so fair - ly, No blue and gold.'

Cathe-rine, her kind - ly com - rade, then did Say, 'Show me too—
'Prince,—and he ne'er has fine a - dorn - ing?' Cath - er - ine cried,

Son of a king must lie so splen-did All gold and blue!'
'Prince, and the Sun, my girl, at morn-ing!' The maid re - plied.

3 'Where, then's his mighty kingdom, say
    you?'
  'Everywhere.'
  'So! and how may I know it, pray you?'
  'Kindness is there.'
  'Kings have bright swords to follow after,
    Bugles to ring?'
  'Nay, here is only children's laughter,
    Here thrushes sing.'

4 'Whom, say now, shall he rule anon? He
    Coming to reign?'
  'Both bird and beast and man, my bonny,
    Mountain and plain.'
  'These shall he hold and have securely—
    How? Tell me, friend?'
  'Only by being a servant, surely,
    Unto the end.'

5 'Susan, who'll herald him, this stranger,
    This kingly boy?'
  'Just a lit star above a manger
    Laughing for joy.'
  'Still, gossip, I might doubt him, maybe,
    Knowing no thing?'
  'Dear my heart, would you doubt a baby
    To be a King?'

QUOI, ma voisine, est-tu fâchée?
    Dis-moi pourquoi.
Veux-tu venir voir l'accouchée
    Avecque moi?
C'est une dame fort discrète,
    Ce m'a-t-on dit,
Qui nous a produit le prophète
    Souvent prédit.

2 Je le veux, allons, ma commère,
    C'est mon désir.
Nous verrons l'enfant et sa mère
    Tout à loisir.
Aurons-nous pas de la dragée
    Et du gâteau?
La salle est-elle bien rangée,
    Y fait-il beau?

3 Ah, ma bergère, tu te trompes
    Bien lourdement;
Elle ne demande pas les pompes
    Ni l'ornement.
Dedans une chétive étable
    Se veut ranger,
Où n'y a ni buffet, ni table
    Pour y manger.

4 Encore faut-il que l'accouchée
    Ait un berceau,
Pour bercer, quand elle est couchée,
    L'enfant nouveau:
N'a-t-elle pas garde et servante
    Pour la servir?
N'est-elle pas assez puissante
    D'y subvenir.

5 L'enfant a pour berceau la crèche
    Pour sommeiller.
Et une botte d'herbe sèche
    Pour oreiller;
Elle a pour boute compagnie
    Son cher baron,
Elle a un boeuf pour sa mégnie
    Et un ânon.

Words written for the older, modal, melody in Henri Lemeignen, *Vieux Noëls* (Nantes, 1876), and in Grimault, of the Angevin carol, 'Quoi ma voisine', a dialogue between two women, here freely paraphrased.

109 O LITTLE ONE

O JESULEIN SÜSS
(GENERAL)
FIRST VERSION

German, S. Scheidt, 1650
Tr. O.B.C.

Ibid.
(M.S.)

SOPRANO
ALTO

1. O lit - tle one sweet, O lit - tle one mild, Thy Fa-ther's pur-pose thou
2. O lit - tle one sweet, O lit - tle one mild, With joy thou hast___ the

TENOR
BASS

hast___ ful - filled; Thou cam'st from heav'n to mor - tal ken, E - qual to
whole world filled; Thou cam - est here from heav'n's do-main, To bring men

be___ with us poor men, O lit - tle one sweet, O lit - tle one mild.
com - fort in their pain, O lit - tle one sweet, O lit - tle one mild.

3 O little one sweet, O little one mild,
   In thee love's beauties are all distilled;
        Then light in us thy love's bright flame,
        That we may give thee back the same,
   O little one sweet, O little one mild.

4 O little one sweet, O little one mild,
   Help us to do as thou hast willed.
        Lo, all we have belongs to thee!
        Ah, keep us in our fealty!
   O little one sweet, O little one mild.

109 O LITTLE ONE
O JESULEIN SÜSS
(GENERAL)
SECOND VERSION

German, S. Scheidt, 1650
Tr. O.B.C.

Ibid.
(harm. J. S. Bach)

1. O lit - tle one sweet, O lit - tle one mild, Thy Fa - ther's
2. O lit - tle one sweet, O lit - tle one mild, With joy thou

pur - pose thou hast ful - filled; Thou cam'st from heav'n to
hast the whole world filled; Thou cam - est here from

mor - tal ken, E - qual to be with us poor
heav'n's do - main, To bring men com - fort in their

men, O lit - tle one sweet, O lit - tle one mild.
pain, O lit - tle one sweet, O lit - tle one mild.

*If sung in conjunction with the first version the melody rhythm of this bar may be altered for the sake of consistency.

Scheidt's version, 'O Jesulein süss, O Jesulein mild, Des Vaters Will'n hast du erfüllt' (see overleaf), is in his *Tabulaturbuch*, 1650. Bach set it as a chorale melody with figured bass in Schemelli's *Gesangbuch*, 1736. The melody appears also in *Seelenharphe* (Halle, 1650) to the words 'Komm, heiliger Geist mit deiner Gnad'.

O JESULEIN süss, O Jesulein mild,
Des Vaters Will'n hast du erfüllt,
Bist kommen aus dem Himmelreich
Uns armen Menschen worden gleich,
O Jesulein süss, O Jesulein mild.

2 O Jesulein süss, O Jesulein mild,
Des Vaters Zorn hast du gestillt.
Du zählst für uns all uns're Schuld
Und schaffst uns deines Vaters Huld,
O Jesulein süss, O Jesulein mild.

3 O Jesulein süss, O Jesulein mild,
Du bist der Lieb' ein Ebenbild.
Zünd an in uns der Liebe Flamm',
Dass wir dich lieben allzusamm,
O Jesulein süss, O Jesulein mild.

110 JESUS OF THE MANGER
(GENERAL)

Pr. Patrick R. Chalmers

Flemish
(M.S.)

1. Sing, good com - pa-ny, frank and free! Je - sus, when so young was
2. Rouse, good com - pa-ny, rouse you, rouse! All the earth to Je - sus
3. Sing, good com - pa-ny, glad and true! God may lodge with me and

he, With the lit - tle calf shared the stall; Low he lay On a
bows; Yet the dwell - ing that he'd im - plore Poor must stay, By my
you; So let's love them— all beasts and men, Kind - li - ly, As doth

day, — on a day, With the lit - tle calf in the
fay, — by my fay, Still the dwell - ing that he'd im -
he, — as doth he; If we love them— all beasts and

stall Low he lay, He lay there— for us all, us all.
-plore Poor must stay— Man's heart on - ly must serve there - for.
men, Kind - li - ly, God will lodge— with us then, ah then!

He lay there— for us all.
Man's heart on - ly there - for.
God will lodge— with us then!

Paraphrase of 'Jesus in den Stal', printed in *Chants Populaires Flamands*, by Lootens and Feys, reprinted by E. Duncan, *Story of the Carol*, and by H. J. L. J. Massé and C. Kennedy Scott, *Book of Old Carols*.

235

111 THE BUILDERS
(GENERAL : DEDICATION)
GRAND DIEU! QUE DE MERVEILLES
(CHRISTMAS)

Pr. Geoffrey Dearmer

Angevin
(M.S.)

1. Sing, all good peo-ple ga-thered, Your voi-ces raise in song With-in this church that fa-thered Our an-cient faith so strong, So tried and wrought to fit-ness In scorn of fire and sword; Sing, as these stones bear wit-ness, Of men who praised the Lord.

2. Each rib from pil-lars spring-ing A froz-en foun-tain plays, A-bove the chan-cel sing-ing In har-mon-y of praise; Like tall trees ev-er grow-ing The diff-ering col-umns stand To bear the vault down-throw-ing The shad-ow of God's hand.

3 At all times and unceasing,
   Work well and truly done,
In loveliness increasing,
   Has mellowed here in one;
The towers and piers unshaken,
   The vaulting finely groined,
Time in his span hath taken
   And in one glory joined.

4 Of wealth and fame and power
   These masons did not know:
'Let's build,' they said, 'a tower,
   Square to the winds that blow;
We are not men of culture,
   Yet we are here to build
Room for a king's sepulture
   And worthy of our guild.'

5 So came each beam and rafter,
   Each wingèd flight of stone.
Their deathless work lives after,
   Their names were never known:
For beauty did they plead not,
   Yet beauty they did win,
And, like a child you heed not,
   The grace of heaven crept in.

6 Here, for a workman's wages,
   This glass so surely stained
Down the long aisles of ages
   In glory has remained.
As brother works with brother
   The glaziers worked to paint
The blue robe of the Mother,
   The red robe of a saint.

7 Proud heads lie here, disowning
   All but a drooping Head;
Whole hands worked here, atoning
   For open Hands that bled;
Full hearts and living voices
   A broken Heart proclaim;
Life after death rejoices,
   And after silence, fame.

GRAND Dieu! Que de merveilles
   S'accomplissent pour moi!
Mes yeux et mes oreilles,
   Rendez-vous à la foi!
La force et la faiblesse,
   La justice et l'amour,
La gloire et la détresse
   S'unissent en ce jour.

2 La lumière immuable
   Est dans l'obscurité;
Je vois dans une étable
   Le Dieu de majesté.
Son trône est une crèche,
   Sa cour, des pastoureaux,
Son silence nous prèche,
   Son mal guérit nos maux.

3 Son enfance sans armes
   En fait un triomphant;
L'enfer est aux alarmes
   Aux cris d'un tendre enfant.
Sa beauté l'épouvante,
   Son nom le fait frémir,
Sa douceur le tourmente
   Ses pleurs le font gémir.

4 Achevez le miracle,
   Adorable vainqueur;
Si j'y mets un obstacle
   Triomphez de mon coeur.
Echauffez-en la glace,
   Brisez sa dureté
Afin qu'y prenne place
   L'ardente charité.

Since the original twenty-two verses of 'Venez à Saint-Maurice' deal in great detail with the characteristics and treasures of Angers Cathedral, the English words have been written for the general idea rather than for the details of the original, and we claim the tune as proper to them only in this most generous and spiritual sense. Topical allusions in the original fix its date as earlier than 1699 and later than 1562. The gay melody has been always attributed to Urbain Renard, but the origin and date of folk-tunes is very doubtful. The carol (which is printed by Grimault in Noëls Angevins) very likely grew up from some humble fiddler seeking alms outside the Cathedral of Saint-Maurice. The alternative words 'Grand Dieu! que de merveilles' are given by Roques.

112 EIA, EIA
(GENERAL)

Cölner Psalter, 1638
Pr. A. G.

Ibid.
(M.S.)

Moderately slow

1. To us in Beth-lem ci - ty Was born a — lit - tle son; In
2. And all our love and for-tune Lie in — his might-y hands; Our

him — all gen - tle gra - ces Were — ga - thered in - to — one,
sor - rows, joys, and fail - ures, He — sees and un - der - stands,

Ei - a, ei - a, Were — ga - thered in - to one.
Ei - a, ei - a, He — sees and — un - der - stands.

3 O Shepherd, ever near us,
　We'll go where thou dost lead;
No matter where the pasture,
　With thee at hand to feed,
　　Eia, eia,
　With thee at hand to feed.

4 No grief shall part us from thee,
　However sharp the edge:
We'll serve, and do thy bidding—
　O take our hearts in pledge!
　　Eia, eia,
　Take thou our hearts in pledge!

Zu Bethlehem geboren
　Ist uns ein Kindelein;
Das hab' ich auserkoren
　Sein Eigen will ich sein,
　　Eia, eia,
　Sein Eigen will ich sein.

3 O Kindelein, von Herzen
　Will ich dich lieben sehr
In Freuden und in Schmerzen
　Je länger, mehr und mehr,
　　Eia, eia,
　Je länger, mehr und mehr.

2 In seine Lieb' versenken
　Will ich mich ganz hinab.
Mein Herz will ich ihm schenken
　Und alles, was ich hab',
　　Eia, eia,
　Und alles, was ich hab'.

4 Dazu dein Gnad' mir gebe
　Bitt' ich aus Herzensgrund,
Dass ich allein dir lebe
　Jetzt und zu aller Stund',
　　Eia, eia,
　Jetzt und zu aller Stund'.

The folk-carol here paraphrased, 'Zu Bethlehem geboren', appears first in print in the *Cölner Psalter*, 1638. Riemann reprinted this version from Nordstern's *Führer zur Seligkeit*, 1671.

238

113 SPANISH CAROL
(NATIVITY)

Tr. J. B. Trend

Galician
(arr. from Pedrell)

1. Up now, lag-gard-ly lass - es, Up, a - wake and a - way!
2. See the tears in his eyes, now; (Sleep, my pret - ty one, sleep!)

Out and gone be-fore cock - crow, On the road be-fore day!
Let him dream when he can, now; (Sleep, my in - no-cent, sleep!)

Ma - ry meek and gen - tle, Rose of Je - ri - cho,
Ah, my pre - cious jew - el, Great the grief and pain,

Bore a babe and laid him In a man - ger low.
Suf - fered through the wide world For the sins of men!

'Panxoliña de Nadal', a Spanish carol from Galicia. The melody is from Pedrell, *Cancionero musical*; the words translated from the *Cancionero popular gallego* of J. Pérez Ballesteros. Cf. No. 81.

TRADITIONAL CAROL TUNES
SET TO OTHER TRADITIONAL OR OLD TEXTS

114 NO ROOM IN THE INN
(ADVENT)

Traditional

Traditional (M.S.)

1. When Cae-sar Au-gust-us had raised a tax-a-tion, He as-sessed all the peo-ple that dwelt in the na-tion; The Jews at that time be-ing un-der Rome's sway Ap-peared in the ci-ty their tri-bute to pay:

2. Then Jo-seph and Ma-ry, who from Da-vid did spring, Went up to the ci-ty of Da-vid their king, And, there be-ing en-tered, cold wel-come they find: From the rich to the poor they are most-ly un-kind.

3 They sought entertainment, but none could they find,
Great numbers of strangers had fillèd the inn;
They knockèd and callèd all this at the door,
But found not a friend where in kind they had store;

4 Their kindred accounted they come were too soon;
'Too late,' said the innkeeper, 'here is no room.'
Amongst strangers and kinsfolk cold welcome they
find —
From the rich to the poor they are mostly unkind.

5 Good Joseph was troubled, but most for his dear,
For her blessèd burden whose time now drew near;
His heart with true sorrow was sorely afflicted
That his virgin spouse was so rudely neglected.

6 He could get no house-room who houses did frame,
But Joseph and Mary must go as they came,
For little is the favour the poor man can find —
From the rich to the poor they are mostly unkind.

7 Whilst the great and the wealthy do frolic in hall,
Possess all the ground-rooms and chambers and all,
Poor Joseph and Mary are thrust in a stable
In Bethlehem city, ground inhospitáble,

8 And with their mean lodging contented they be:
For the minds of the just with their fortunes agree;
They bear all affronts with their meekness of mind,
And be not offended though the rich be unkind.

9 O Bethlehem, Bethlehem, welcome this stranger
That was born in a stable and laid in a manger;
For he is a physician to heal all our smarts—
Come welcome, sweet Jesus, and lodge in our hearts.

This simple and charming carol was probably sung to one of the traditional 'Virgin unspotted' tunes (cf. No. 4). We have chosen the one printed by Sandys in 1833. The text is also from Sandys, very slightly altered.

115 JOSEPH AND MARY
(ADVENT AND CHRISTMAS)

Traditional

English traditional
(R.V.W.)

1. O, Jo - seph being an old man tru - ly, He ___ mar - ried a vir - gin fair and free; A pur - er vir - gin could no man see Than he chose ___ for his ___ wife and his dear - est ___

- to ___ the place where he was ___ born, Un - -to ___ the Em-per-or to be sworn, To pay ___ a tri - bute that's du - ly known, Both ___ for ___ him - self ___ and his ___ dear - est ___

were they con - strain - ed pre - sent - ly With - -in ___ a sta - ble all night to lie, Where they ___ did ox - en and as - ses tie, With ___ his ___ true love ___ and his ___ dear - est ___

dear.
dear.
dear.

2. They liv - - ed both in joy and bliss; But
4. And when they were to Beth - le-hem come, The
6. The king of all power was in Beth - le-hem born, Who

now a strict com-mand-ment is, In Jew - ry - land no
inns were filled, both all and some; For Jo - seph en - treated them,
wore for our sakes a crown of thorn. Then God pre-serve us both

man should miss To go a - -long with his
ev - 'ry one, Both for him - self and his
even and morn For Je - sus' sake, our

1st time   *Last time*

dear - est dear,
dear - est dear.
dear - est dear!

3. Un-
5. Then

ARRANGEMENT FOR UNACCOMPANIED VOICES

1. O, Jo - seph being an old man tru - ly, He__
2. They liv - ed both__ in joy and__ bliss; But__

NOTE. The words to be sung by the tenors only,
the other parts to vocalize.

mar-ried a vir - gin fair and free; A pur - - er vir - gin could
now__ a strict com - mand-ment is, In Jew - - ry - land__ no

no man see Than he chose for his__ wife and his dear - - est dear.
man should miss To__ go a - long__with his__ dear - - est__ dear,

3 Unto the place where he was born,
   Unto the Emperor to be sworn,
   To pay a tribute that's duly known,
   Both for himself and his dearest dear.

4 And when they were to Bethlehem come,
   The inns were filled, both all and some;
   For Joseph entreated them, every one,
   Both for himself and his dearest dear.

5 Then were they constrainèd presently
   Within a stable all night to lie,
   Where they did oxen and asses tie,
   With his true love and his dearest dear.

6 The king of all power was in Bethlehem born,
   Who wore for our sakes a crown of thorn.
   Then God preserve us both even and morn
   For Jesus' sake, our dearest dear!

The original words ('There is a fountain') to which Mrs. Esther Smith sung this tune at Weobley were probably not traditional, and were moreover full of the rather unpleasant imagery which is characteristic of much of the eighteenth-century evangelistic verse. They are printed in the *Journal of the Folk-Song Society*, ii. 133 and iv. 21. Rather than omit such a fine tune, the Editors of *Twelve Traditional Carols from Herefordshire* decided to set other words to it—undoubtedly traditional, for which, as far as they know, no tune has been preserved, and we have done the same. These words are taken from Sandys. They seem to reach back to the seventeenth century; but the story of Joseph's doubts (here omitted from the sixteen verses of the original) was familiar in the fourteenth, and occurs in a different carol of the fifteenth century. See E. Rickert, *Ancient English Christmas Carols*, xix. 24-7.

116 A BABE IS BORN
(CHRISTMAS: EPIPHANY)

Nowell, el, el, el,
Now is well, that ever was woe.

15th century

English traditional
(M.S.)

1. A babe is born all of a may, To
2. At Beth - le - hem, that bless - - ed place, The

bring sal - va - tion un - to us. To him we sing both
child of bliss now born he_ was; And him to serve God

night and_ day *Ve - ni cre - a - tor Spi - ri - tus.*
give us_ grace, *O lux be - a - ta Tri - ni - tas.*

3 There came three kings out of the East,
   To worship the King that is so free,
   With gold and myrrh and frankincense,
    A solis ortus cardine.

4 The shepherds heard an angel's cry,
   A merry song that night sung he.
   'Why are ye so sore aghast?'
    Jam ortus solis cardine.

5 The angels came down with one cry,
   A fair song that night sung they
   In the worship of that child:
    Gloria tibi Domine.

1. may—maid. *Veni creator*—Come, creator Spirit: the Whitsun hymns, *E.H.* 153, 154, 156.
2. *O lux beata*—O Trinity, blessed light: Evening hymn, *E.H.* 164. 3. *A solis ortus cardine*—Risen
from the quarter of the sun: Christmas hymn, *E.H.* 18. 4. Orig. 'The herdes heardyn'. 5. *Gloria
tibi Domine*—Glory to thee, O Lord.
   Sloane MS. 2593, first half of the fifteenth century. Another version in Richard Hill's MS. (cf. No.
36), 'There is a child born of a may'. We have altered, in v. 1, 'In the savasyoun of us', with Bramley
and Stainer, who preserved the tune, and in 4, 'A merye song then sungyn he', and similarly in 5.
Greene: 122(b).

117 IMMORTAL BABE
(CHRISTMAS: EPIPHANY)

Bishop Joseph Hall

German, 16th century
(M.S.)

1. Im - mor - tal babe, who this dear day Didst change thine hea - ven for our clay, And didst with flesh thy god - head veil, E - ter - nal Son of God, all hail!

2. Shine, hap - py star: ye an - gels sing Glo - ry on high to hea - ven's King: Run, shep - herds, leave your night - ly watch, See heav'n come down to Beth - lem's cratch.

3 Worship, ye sages of the East,
The King of gods in meanness dressed:
O blessèd maid, smile and adore
The God thy womb and arms have bore.

4 Star, angels, shepherds, and wise sages,
Thou virgin glory of all ages,
Restorèd frame of heaven and earth,
Joy in your dear Redeemer's birth!

2. cratch—cradle.
From *The Shaking of the Olive Tree*, by Joseph Hall, Bishop of Exeter, 1660. The melody is a German traditional carol tune.

118 SUSANNI
(CHRISTMAS : EPIPHANY)

15th century

German
(M.S.)

1. A lit-tle child there is— y-born, Ei - - a,— ei - - a, su-san-ni, su-san-ni, su - san - ni. And he sprang out of Jes - se's thorn, Al - le - lu - ya, al--le--lu-ya, To save— all us — that were— for-lorn.

2. Now Je-sus is the child-es name, Ei - - a,— ei - - a, su-san-ni, su-san-ni, su - san - ni. And Ma - ry mild she is— his dame; Al - le - lu - ya, al--le--lu-ya, And so— our sor-row is turned— to game.

248

3 It fell upon the high midnight,
   Eia, eia, etc.
The stars they shone both fair and bright,
   Alleluya, alleluya
The angels sang with all their might.

4 *Three kings there came with their presénts
   Eia, eia, etc.
Of myrrh and gold and frankincense,
   Alleluya, alleluya
As clerkès sing in their sequence.

5 Now sit we down upon our knee,
   Eia, eia, etc.
And pray we to the Trinity,
   Alleluya, alleluya,
Our help, our succour for to be.

Vom Himmel hoch, o Engel, kommt!
Eia, eia, susanni, susanni, susanni.
Kommt singt und klingt, kommt pfeift und trombt,
   Alleluya, alleluya,
   Von Jesus singt und Maria.

2 Kommt ohne Instrumenten nit,
   Eia, eia, usw.
Bringt Lauten, Harfen, Geigen mit!
   Alleluya, alleluya,
   Von Jesus singt und Maria.

3 Lasst hören euer Stimmen viel
   Eia, eia, usw.
Mit' Orgel und mit Saitenspiel!
   Alleluya, alleluya,
   Von Jesus singt und Maria.

4 Sehr süss muss sein der Orgel Klang,
   Eia, eia, usw.
Süss über allen Vögelsang.
   Alleluya, alleluya,
   Von Jesus singt und Maria.

5 Das Lautenspiel muss lauten süss,
   Eia, eia, usw.
Davon das Kindlein schlafen müss.
   Alleluya, alleluya,
   Von Jesus singt und Maria.

6 Singt Fried' den Menschen weit und breit,
   Eia, eia, usw.
Gott Preis und Ehr' in Ewigkeit.
   Alleluya, alleluya, .
   Von Jesus singt und Maria.

Ashmolean MS. 1393. Printed *Early Bodleian Music*, 1901, Greene, No. 35, and Chambers and Sidgwick; here collated with Richard Hill's MS. The proper tune is, however, unknown: we have therefore used the melody of a similar carol, 'Susanni, Susanni' (Vom Himmel hoch); the refrain is that of this German carol, which is given in Hölscher's *Niederdeutsche geistliche Lieder* (Berlin, 1854) from a source of 1588, but is of earlier origin.

119 ANGELS, FROM THE REALMS
LES ANGES DANS NOS CAMPAGNES
(CHRISTMAS: EPIPHANY)

J. Montgomery

French
(M.S.)

1. An-gels, from the realms of glo-ry, Wing your flight o'er all the earth;
2. Shep-herds in the field a-bid-ing, Watch-ing o'er your flocks by night,

Ye who sang cre-a-tion's sto-ry Now pro-claim Mes-si-ah's birth:
God with man is now re-sid-ing; Yon-der shines the in-fant Light:

*Come_____ and wor-ship
*Glo-ria

Christ the new-born King,_____ Come_____
in ex-cel-sis De-o, Glo-

*alternative refrain

250

and_ wor - ship, Wor- ship Christ the new - born King.
- - - - - ria in ex - cel - sis De - - - o.

and wor - ship, Wor- ship Christ the new - born King.
- - - - - ria in ex - cel - sis De - - - o.

3 Sages, leave your contemplations;
  Brighter visions beam afar;
  Seek the great Desire of Nations;
  Ye have seen his natal star:
  Come and worship, etc.

4 Saints before the altar bending,
  Watching long in hope and fear,
  Suddenly the Lord, descending,
  In his temple shall appear:
  Come and worship, etc.

5 Though an infant now we view him,
  He shall fill his Father's throne,
  Gather all the nations to him;
  Every knee shall then bow down:
  Come and worship, etc.

Les anges dans nos campagnes
  Ont entonné l'hymne des cieux;
Et l'écho de nos montagnes
  Redit ce chant mélodieux:
    Gloria in excelsis Deo.

2 Bergers, pour qui cette fête?
    Quel est l'objet de tous ces chants?
  Quel vainqueur, quelle conquête
    Mérite ces cris triomphants?
      Gloria in excelsis Deo.

3 Ils annoncent la naissance
    Du libérateur d'Israël,
  Et, pleins de reconnaissance,
    Chantent en ce jour solennel:
      Gloria in excelsis Deo.

4 Bergers, loin de vos retraites
    Unissez-vous à leurs concerts
  Et que vos tendres musettes
    Fassent retentir dans les airs:
      Gloria in excelsis Deo.

5 Cherchons tous l'heureux village
    Qui l'a vu naître sous ses toits,
  Offrons-lui le tendre hommage
    Et de nos coeurs et nos voix!
      Gloria in excelsis Deo.

Montgomery's well-known hymn, first printed in his newspaper *Iris*, December 24, 1816, and included among 'Three New Carols' in *The Christmas Box*, 1825 (the first complete book of the Religious Tract Society, and precursor of the popular 'Christmas Books'), reads almost like an early nineteenth-century translation of the opening verses of 'Les anges dans nos campagnes', the old French carol from which we take the tune. The fifth verse is taken from 'The Babe of Bethlehem', another carol in *The Christmas Box*. The refrain 'Gloria in excelsis Deo' may well be preferred in the English version also.

120 IN BETHLEHEM, THAT FAIR CITY
(CHRISTMAS: INNOCENTS' DAY)

To bliss God bring us, all and some,
Christe redemptor omnium.

15th century

14th century
(G. S.)

1. In Beth - le - hem, that fair ci - ty,
2. Lord and prince of high de - gree,

Al - le - - - -lu - - - ya,

Was born a child that was so free,

Jam lu - cis or - to si - de -re.

Al - le - - - - - - - - - - lu - ya.

ALTERNATIVE VERSION (MELODY IN TENOR)

3. Je - su, for the love of thee,
4. In Beth - le - hem, that fair ci - ty,

Al - le - - -

Child - ren were slain in great plen-
- *lu* - - - *ya,* *A so* - *lis or* - *tus car* - *di* -

-ty,
-*ne.* *Al* - *le* - - - - - - - - - - - - *lu* - *ya.*

3 Jesu, for the love of thee,
   Children were slain in great plenty,

4 In Bethlehem, that fair city,
   A solis ortus cardine.

5 As the sun shineth through the glass,
   So Jesu in her body was.

6 Then him to serve God give us grace,
   O lux beata Trinitas.

7 Now is he born our Lord Jesus,
   He that made merry all of us:

8 Then be all merry in this house,
   Exultet coelum laudibus.

Christe, &c.—Christ, redeemer of all (Christmas Mattins hymn, *E.H.* 17). 2. *Jam lucis, &c.*—'Now that the daylight fills the sky' (Prime, *E.H.* 254). 4. *A solis, &c.* and 6. *O lux, &c.*—See No. 23. 8. *Exultet, &c.*—Let heaven exult with praises, *E.H.* 176.
   There are different versions of this carol in the fifteenth-century Cambridge T.C.C. (O 3. 58) MS., in Richard Hill's MS., &c. These different versions are printed in Fuller Maitland, Wright, Chambers and Sidgwick, and Greene, No. 21. The refrain belongs to the fourteenth-century melody of 'Puer natus in Bethlehem', of which there are very many variants, the earliest (fifteenth century) MSS., being at Strassburg and Munich. Our version of the tune appears in *Piae Cantiones,* and was harmonized by Bach (1685-1750). Compare No. 85, which gives Bach's harmonization, and the original German words.

121 FALAN-TIDING
(EPIPHANY: CHRISTMAS)

c. 1610

Tyrolese
(M.S.)

SOPRANO
ALTO

TENOR
BASS

1. Out of the o-rient crys-tal_skies A blaz-ing star did shine, Show-
2. This shin-ing star three kings did_guide Even from the furth-est East, To
3. And for the joy of his great birth A thou-sand an-gels sing: 'Glo-

-ing the place where poor - ly_ lies A_ bless - ed babe di - vine, Born
Beth - le - hem where it be - tide This_ bless - ed babe did rest, Laid
-ry and peace un - to the_earth Where born is this new King!' The

of a maid of roy - al blood Who Ma - ry hight by name, A
in a sil - ly man - ger poor, Be - twixt an ox and ass, Whom
shep - herds dwell - ing there a - bout, When they this news did know, Came

sa - cred rose which once did_ bud By grace of heav'n - ly flame.
these three kings did all a - dore As God's high plea - sure was.
sing - ing all even in a_rout, 'Fal - an - ti - ding - di - do!'

2. silly—simple.

254

ALTERNATIVE WORDS

THE wise may bring their learning,
   The rich may bring their wealth;
And some may bring their greatness,
   And some bring strength and health:
We too would bring our treasures
   To offer to the King;
We have no wealth or learning,
   What shall we pilgrims bring?

2 We'll bring him hearts that love him,
   We'll bring him thankful praise,
And mortals, daily striving
   To walk in holy ways:
And these shall be the treasures
   We offer to the King,
And these are gifts that even
   The humblest soul may bring.

3 We'll bring the many duties
   We have to do each day;
We'll try our best to please him,
   In all we do and say:
And better are these treasures
   To offer to our King
Than richest gifts without them;
   Yet these we all may bring.

In the B.M. Add. MS. 29401, with a contemporary five-part setting; as this is a motet we are not including it, but have used the tune of a Tyrolese carol, 'Ihr Hirten, stehet alle auf'. The alternative English words are from *Book of Praise for Children* (1881).

122 HERRICK'S CAROL
(CHRISTMAS)

Robert Herrick (1647)

German
(M.S.)

and his showers Turns all the pa - tient ground to flowers.

3 The darling of the world is come,
And fit it is we find a room
To welcome him. The nobler part
Of all the house here is the heart:

We see him come, etc.

4 Which we will give him, and bequeath
This holly and this ivy wreath,
To do him honour who's our King,
And Lord of all this revelling:

We see him come, etc.

Herrick's *Hesperides,* from which these words are taken, was performed before Charles I, 'in the Presence, at Whitehall'. The words are here arranged for 'Als ich bei meinen Schafen wacht', a Christmas-play carol in the *Cölner Gesangbuch* (1623), and elsewhere, reprinted in Böhme. The original words do not fit this arrangement, but a literal translation ('As I was watching by my sheep') will be found in *Songs for all Seasons* (O.U.P.).

123 CHANTICLEER
(NATIVITY)

W. Austin

English traditional
(M.S.)

1. All this night shrill chan-ti-cleer, Day's pro-claim-ing trum-pet-er,
2. Wake, O earth, wake ev-'ry— thing! Wake and hear the joy I bring;
3. Hail, O Sun, O bless-ed— Light, Sent in-to the world by night!

Claps his wings and loud-ly cries, Mor-tals, mor-tals,— wake and rise!
Wake and joy; for all this night Heav'n and ev-'ry— twink-ling light,
Let thy rays and heav'n-ly powers Shine in these dark— souls of ours;

See a won-der Heav'n is un-der; From the earth— is—
All a-maz-ing, Still stand gaz-ing. An- -gels, powers, and—
For most du-ly Thou art tru-ly God and man,— we—

Shines— all— night, though day be done.
Wake,— and joy this Sun to see.
Hail,— O— Sun of Right - - -eous -ness!

risen a Sun Shines all night, though day be done.
all that be, Wake, and joy this Sun to see.
do con-fess: Hail, O Sun of Right-eous - -ness!

Shines all night, though day be done.
Wake, and joy this Sun to see.
Hail, O Sun of Right - -eous - -ness!

From 'Devotionis Augustinianae Flamma by William Austin, of Lincolnes Inne Esquier', who died 16 January 1633 (published, 1635). There is a monument to him in St. Saviour's, Southwark. The tune is adapted from an English traditional melody.

124 SUMMER IN WINTER
(NATIVITY)

R.Crashaw

Alsatian
(M.S.)

1. Gloo-my night em-braced the place___ Where the no-ble
   in-fant lay; The babe looked up and shewed_ his face, In
   spite of dark-ness it ___ was day! It was___ thy day, sweet,
   and___ did rise, Not from the East, but from___ thine eyes.

2. Win-ter chid a-loud,___ and sent The an-gry North to
   wage___ his wars. The North for-got his fierce___ in-tent, And
   left per-fumes, in-stead___ of scars. By those___ sweet eyes' per-
   -sua-sive powers Where he meant frost, he scat-tered flowers.

3 We saw thee in thy balmy nest,
  Bright Dawn of our eternal day!
We saw thine eyes break from their east
  And chase the trembling shades away;
We saw thee, and we blessed the sight,
We saw thee by thine own sweet light.

4 Welcome, all wonders in one sight,
  Eternity shut in a span,
Summer in winter, day in night,
  Heaven in earth, and God in man!
Great little one! whose all-embracing birth
Lifts earth to heaven, stoops heaven to earth.

From the eighteen stanzas of Crashaw's 'Hymn in the
Holy Nativity', 1648. The melody is from *Cantiques de Strasbourg*, 1697.

125 RORATE
(NATIVITY)

William Dunbar

Scottish traditional

1. Ro - ra - te coe - li de - su - per! Hea - vens, dis - til your
2. Sin - ners be - glad, and pen - ance do, And thank your Ma - ker

bal - my showers; For now is risen the bright Day - star, From
heart - ful - ly; For he that ye might not come to, To

the rose Ma - ry, flower of flowers: The clear Sun, whom no
you is co - men full hum - bly, Your soul - es with his

cloud de - vours, Sur - mount - ing Phoe - bus in the east, Is
blood to - buy, And loose you of the fiend's ar - rest, And

260

co - men of his— heav'n-ly— towers, *Et*— *no - bis pu - er— na - tus est.*
on - ly of his— own mer - cy; *Pro*— *no - bis pu - er— na - tus est*

3 Celestial fowlès in the air,
   Sing with your notès upon height,
   In firthès and in forests fair
   Be mirthful now at all your might;
   For passèd is your dully night;
   Aurora has the cloudès pierced,
   The sun is risen with gladsome light,
   Et nobis puer natus est.

4 Sing, heaven imperial, most of height,
   Regions of air make harmony,
   All fish in flood and fowl of flight
   Be mirthful and make melody:
   All *Gloria in excelsis* cry,

   ♪ | ♩

   Heaven, earth, sea, man, bird, and beast;
   He that is crowned above the sky
   Pro nobis puer natus est.

1. *Rorate*, &c.—Drop down, ye heavens, from above (Is. 45, 8). *Et nobis*, &c.—And for us a boy is born.
   On the eve of the 'Reformation, Dunbar, the Scottish diplomat, ex-Franciscan, and poet, still uses the sounded 'e' when he thinks fit; he is, as Palgrave says, 'the fine flower of expiring medievalism'. The verses are here set to a little-known Scottish melody.

126 CANDLEMAS EVE
(1 FEBRUARY, AND SPRING)

R. Herrick

Church-gallery book
(M.S.)

1. Down with the rose-ma-ry and bays, Down with the mis-tle-toe; In-stead of hol-ly, — now up-raise The — green-er box, for show. 2. The — hol-ly hith-er-to did sway: Let — box now dom-in-eer Un-til the dan-cing Eas-ter Day, Or — Eas-ter's Eve ap-pear.

3. Then youth-ful box, which now hath grace Your hou-ses to re-new, Grown old, sur-ren-der — must his place Un-to the crisp-ed yew. 4. When yew is out, then birch comes in, And — ma-ny flowers be-side, Both of a fresh — and fra-grant kin, To — hon-our Whit-sun-tide.

5. Green rush-es then, and sweet-est bents, With cool-er oak-en boughs, Come in for come-ly — or-na-ments, To — re-a-dorn the house. 6. Thus times do shift, thus times do shift; each — thing his turn does hold; New things suc-ceed, — new things suc-ceed, as — form-er things grow old.

The tune is from an old church-gallery book, discovered by the Rev. L. J. T. Darwall.

127 GOD IS ASCENDED

GEN HIMMEL AUFGEFAHREN IST
(ASCENSION)

Henry More

German, 16th century
(M.S.)

1. God is as - cen - ded up on high, Al - le - lu -
2. And prince - ly seat - ed in the sky, Al - le - lu -

- ya,———— Al - le - lu - ya.

With mer - ry noise of
Rules ov - er all the

trum - pet's sound,
world a - round. Al - le - lu - ya,———— Al - le - lu - ya.

3 In human flesh and shape he went,
Alleluya.
Adornèd with his passion's scars,
Alleluya.

4 Which in heaven's sight he did present
Alleluya.
More glorious than the glittering stars.
Alleluya.

5 Lord, raise our sinking minds therefore
Alleluya.
Up to our proper country dear,
Alleluya.

6 And purify us evermore,
Alleluya.
To fit us for those regions clear.
Alleluya.

GEN Himmel aufgefahren ist, *Alleluya.*
Der König der Ehren, Jesus Christ, *Alleluya.*

2 Er sitzt zur rechten Gottes Hand, *Alleluya.*
Herrscht über Himmel und alle Land. *Alleluya.*

3 Zwei Engel sagten offenbar, *Alleluya.*
'Ihr Galiläer, nehmet wahr:' *Alleluya.*

4 'Jesus, der von euch ist genommen,' *Alleluya.*
Die Welt zu richten wird er kommen. *Alleluya.*

5 Der Gläubigen hat er bereit't, *Alleluya.*
Einen Weg zu der Seeligkeit. *Alleluya.*

6 Zu dieser freudenreicher Zeit, *Alleluya.*
Sei Gott gelobt in Ewigkeit. *Alleluya.*

The German text and melody of 'Gen Himmel aufgefahren ist' are in David Corner, 1631, as 'Ein altes Lobgesang von Christi Himmelfahrt'. More's first stanza almost exactly reproduces the short text of the original as reprinted in Riemann. Henry More, the saintly Cambridge Platonist, became Fellow of Christ's College in 1639.

128 WELCOME, SUMMER

Geoffrey Chaucer

Irish traditional
(M.S.)

Moderately quick

SOPRANO
ALTO

Solo: 1. Now wel-come, Sum - mer, with thy sun - ne soft,
Chorus: 2. Saint Val - en - tine that art full high on loft,
Solo: 3. Well have they cau - se for to glad - den oft,
Solo: 4. 'Now wel-come, Sum - mer, with thy sun - ne soft,

TENOR
BASS

Chorus: Now wel - come, Sum - mer, with thy sun - ne soft,
Thus sing - en smal - le fowl - es for thy sake
Chorus: Well have they cau - se for to glad - den oft,
Chorus: Now wel - come, Sum - mer, with thy sun - ne soft,

That ____ hast this win - ter's wea - thers o - ver - shake
'Now ____ wel - come, Sum - mer, with thy sun - ne soft,
Since ____ each of them re - - cov - ered hath his make;
That ____ hast this win - ter's wea - thers o - ver - shake

And driven a - way the lon - ge night - es black.
That hast this win - ter's wea - thers o - ver - shake.'
Full bliss - ful may they sing - en when they wake—
And driven a - way the lon - ge night - es black.'

1. overshake—shaken off. 2. on loft—in the air. fowlès (foules)—birds. 3. gladden—rejoice.
make—mate.
This roundel comes at the end of *The Parlement of Foules*. We have set it to an old Irish carol tune,
slightly adapted.

264

129 PLEASURE IT IS
(SUMMER AND HARVEST)

William Cornish

B. Waldis (1553)
(M. S.)

In moderate time

Plea - sure it is___ To hear, I wis, The bir - des sing. The deer in the dale, The sheep in the vale, The corn_ spring-ing; God's pur-vey-ance For sus-te-nance It is for man. Then we al-ways To him give praise, And thank_ him then, and thank_ him then.

William Cornish, or Cornysshe, was Master of the Chapel Royal under Henry VII and Henry VIII, for whom he composed music and acted in court pageants; in 1518 he forced Wolsey to give up one of his choristers to the Chapel Royal. The words occur in a book of which only one copy is known to exist (B.M., K. 1, e. 1), 'Bassus. In this boke ar cōteynyd XX sōgs, IX of IIII partes and XI of thre partes', printed in 1530, not by Wynkyn de Worde, as was formerly assumed, but by an unknown printer, whose colophon, together with the title-leaf of the missing Medius part, was discovered in a binding at Westminster Abbey. The melody is lost, only the bass part being given in Bassus: the words are here set to B. Waldis's tune for Ps. 124 (1553), printed by Zahn, no. 5571.

130 WATTS'S CRADLE SONG
(GENERAL)

Isaac Watts

Northumbrian
(Freely arr. M.S.)

Rather slowly, but with flowing movement

1. Hush! my dear, lie still and slum-ber; Ho - ly an-gels guard thy bed!
   Heav'n-ly bless-ings with-out num-ber Gent-ly fall-ing on thy head.
2. Sleep, my babe; thy food and rai-ment, House and home, thy friends pro-vide;
   All with-out thy care and pay-ment, All thy wants are well sup-plied.

SOPRANO
ALTO

VERSES 1 & 2 (Verse 1 sung as a soprano solo unaccompanied.
Verse 2, the words sung by sopranos, other parts hum accompaniment.)

TENOR
BASS

VERSE 3 (all sing words)

3. How much bet - ter thou'rt at - ten- ded Than the Son of God could be____

When from hea - ven he de - scend-ed, And be - came a child like thee.____

VERSE 4
(S. & A.) Hush! my dear, lie still and slum - ber;

Melody 4. Soft and ea - sy is thy cra - dle; Coarse and hard thy Sa - viour lay,
in Tenor: When his birth-place was a sta - ble And his soft-est bed was hay.

VERSE 5

5. See the love-ly babe ad-dress-ing: Love-ly in-fant, how he smiled!

When he wept, the mo-ther's bless-ing Soothed and hushed the ho-ly— child.

rit. e dim.

VERSE 6 _a tempo_

Hush! my dear, lie still and slum-ber;

Melody in Alto 6. { Lo, he slum-bers in his man-ger, Where the horn-ed ox-en fed;
Peace, my dar-ling! here's no dan-ger; Here's no ox a-near thy bed.

Hush! my dear, lie still and slum-ber;

VERSE 7

7. Mayst thou live to know and fear_him, Trust and love him all thy days:

Then go dwell for ev-er near_him, See his face and sing his praise, and sing his praise.

Copyright, 1928, by Martin Shaw

Watts's words are here set to a traditional carol tune, sung to
these words, and noted in Northumberland by R. Vaughan Williams.

131 COVERDALE'S CAROL
(GENERAL)

Miles Coverdale

English traditional
(R.V.W.)

Lento (In free rhythm)

VOICES IN UNISON

1. Now bless-ed be thou, Christ Je-su, Thou
2. E-ter-nal light doth now_ ap-pear Un-
5. All this_ did he for us_ free-ly, For

ACCPT.

p

art man born, __ and this is __ true: With
-to the world__ both far and_ near; It
to de-clare__ his great mer-cy. All

our__ poor_ flesh__ and_ our poor blood, Was-
shin-eth__ clear__ even_ at mid-night, Mak-
Christ-en-dom __ be_ mer-ry there-fore, And_

1st time   Last time
rall.

colla voce

clothed that ev - er - last - ing Good.
-ing__ us child - ren of his light. 2.) E-
give__ him thanks for__

ev - er - more!

ARRANGEMENT FOR UNACCOMPANIED VOICES

(The words to be sung by sopranos only; the other parts to vocalize)

3. The Lord__ Christ Je - sus, God's__ Son__ dear, Was
4. In - to_____ this world right poor__ came__ he, To

once a guest__ and stran - ger__ here, Us for__ to__ bring__ from
make us rich__ in his mer - cy; There - fore__ would he__ our__

mi - se - ry, That__ we__ might live__ e - ter - nal - ly.
sins for - give, That__ we__ with him__ in__ heav'n might live.

The melody was noted from Mrs. Esther Smith, Dilwyn, sung by her to the strange carol or song about the farmer who ploughed on Christmas Day—see *Twelve Traditional Carols from Herefordshire*, E. M. Leather and R. Vaughan Williams (Stainer & Bell). The words (slightly altered) are a transla- tion of 'Gelobet seist du Jesu Christ' from Coverdale's *Goostly Psalmes and Spiritualle Songes*, 1546: the unique copy is at Queen's College, Oxford, reprinted by the Parker Society.

132 PSALM OF SION
(GENERAL)

W. Prid (1585)

English traditional
(R.V.W.)

1. O mo - ther dear, Je - ru - sa - lem, Je -
2. O come - ly queen, in glo - ry clad, In

- ho - vah's throne on high,___ O sa - cred ci - ty,
hon - our and de - gree;___ All fair thou art, ex -

queen, and wife Of Christ___ e - ter - nal - ly!___
- ceed - ing bright, No spot___ there is in thee.___

270

3 Thy part, thy shape, thy stately grace,
   Thy favour fair in deed,
Thy pleasant hue and countenance,
   All others doth exceed.

4 O then thrice happy, should my state
   In happiness remain,
If I might once thy glorious seat
   And princely place attain,

5 And view thy gallant gates, thy walls,
   Thy streets and dwellings wide,
Thy noble troop of citizens
   And mighty King beside.

6 He is the King of kings, beset
   Amidst his servants' right;
And they his happy household all
   Do serve him day and night.

7 O mother dear, Jerusalem,
   The comfort of us all,
How sweet thou art and delicate;
   No thing shall thee befall!

Versions of the New Jerusalem Hymn formed part of English folk-carol singing from the end of the sixteenth century onwards, and sometimes fragments strayed into other carols (as in No. 46). There are two originals, that by Prid in *The Glasse of vaine-glorie: Faithfully translated (out of S. Augustine his booke intituled Speculum peccatoris)*, by W. Prid, Doctor of the Laws, printed by J. Windel, London, 1585; and the less close paraphrase of Augustine in the British Museum MS., by 'F. B. P.', beginning 'Jerusalem, my happy home', about the same date. Versions appeared in the broadsides: Julian describes an English one of *c.* 1660, and a Scottish one of the eighteenth century, which latter combines Prid with 'F. B. P.' The version of 1801 attributed to Montgomery in the *Oxford Hymn Book* is probably by Joseph Bromehead.

   'F. B. P.'s' version was sung to the tune 'Diana', of which one part only has been discovered. The *c.* 1660 version was sung to 'O man in desperation'. We have used the old carol tune, 'Saint Austin' ('In Pescod time', Chappell), which is set in the *English Hymnal* (638) and *Songs of Praise* (395) to the 'F. B. P.' version.

PART III
MODERN TEXTS
WRITTEN FOR OR ADAPTED TO TRADITIONAL TUNES

133 CAROL OF THE ADVENT
(NOVEMBER AND DECEMBER)

SHEPHERDS, SHAKE OFF YOUR DROWSY SLEEP
(CHRISTMAS)

Eleanor Farjeon
(alternative words : Anon.)

Besançon
(M.S.)

1. Peo-ple, look East. The time is near Of the

crown - ing of__ the year. Make your house fair as you are

a - ble, Trim_ the hearth, and set__ the ta - ble. Peo-ple, look

CHORUS

*(alternative version)** Shep-herds, the*

* for use with alternative words only

East,   and sing   to - day: Love the Guest is on _ the way.
cho - rus come   and swell, Sing No - el,   No - el, _ No - el!

Peo-ple, look East,_____   Love the Guest _ is on   the way.
Shep-herds, the cho - rus swell, Sing No - el,   No - el,   No - el!

Peo-ple, look East,   Love   is   on   the way.
Come_ and swell,   Sing No - el, No - el!

Peo- ple, look East, Love the Guest   is on   the way.
Come_ and swell, Sing No - el,   No - el,   No - el!

2 Furrows, be glad. Though earth is bare,
One more seed is planted there:
Give up your strength the seed to nourish,
That in course the flower may flourish.
  People, look East, and sing today:
  Love the Rose is on the way.

3 Birds, though ye long have ceased to build,
Guard the nest that must be filled.
Even the hour when wings are frozen
He for fledging-time has chosen.
  People, look East, and sing today:
  Love the Bird is on the way.

4 Stars, keep the watch. When night is dim
One more light the bowl shall brim,
Shining beyond the frosty weather,
Bright as sun and moon together.
  People, look East, and sing today:
  Love the Star is on the way.

5 Angels, announce to man and beast
Him who cometh from the East.
Set every peak and valley humming
With the word, the Lord is coming.
  People, look East, and sing today:
  Love the Lord is on the way.

ALTERNATIVE WORDS

SHEPHERDS, shake off your drowsy sleep,
Rise, and leave your silly sheep;
Angels from heaven around are singing,
Tidings of great joy are bringing.

  Shepherds, the chorus come and swell,
  Sing Noel, Noel, Noel!

2 Hark! even now the bells ring round,
Listen to their merry sound;
Hark! how the birds new songs are making,
As if winter's chains were breaking.
  Shepherds, the chorus etc.

3 See how the flowers all burst anew,
Thinking snow is summer dew;
See how the stars afresh are glowing,
All their brightest beams bestowing.
  Shepherds, the chorus etc.

4 Cometh at length the age of peace,
Strife and sorrow now shall cease;
Prophets foretold the wondrous story
Of this heaven-born Prince of glory.
  Shepherds, the chorus etc.

5 Shepherds! then up and quick away,
Seek the babe ere break of day;
He is the hope of every nation,
All in him shall find salvation.
  Shepherds, the chorus etc.

The tune is an old Besançon carol tune, 'Chantons, bargiés, Noué, Noué' (cf. No. 106) which appeared with the words 'Shepherds, shake off your drowsy sleep' in Bramley and Stainer's collection.
Michel Corrette uses this melody in his XVIth Concerto Comique (1733) under the title 'V'la ce que c'est que d'aller au bois'.

273

134 IF YE WOULD HEAR
(ADVENT: CHRISTMAS EVE)

Dora Greenwell

Dutch
(Adapted R.V.W. and M.S.)

VERSES 1, 2, 4, & 6 **With movement**

1. If ye would hear the an - - gels sing
2. If ye would hear the an - - gels sing,
4. If ye would hear the an - - gels sing,
6. If ye would hear the an - - gels sing,

'Peace on earth and mer - cy mild',___ Think__ of him who was
Rise, and spread your Christ - mas fare; 'Tis merr - ier still___ the
Rise, and light your Christ - mas fire; And see that ye pile__ the
Christ - ians! See ye let each door Stand wid - - er than it e'er

once a child,
more that share,
logs still higher
stood be - fore,

On Christ - mas Day in the morn - - ing.

VERSES 3, 5, & 7

3. Rise, and bake— your Christ-mas bread: Christ-ians, rise!_ The
5. Rise, and light— your Christ-mas fire; Christ-ians, rise!_ The
7. Rise, and o-pen wide the door; Christ-ians, rise!_ The

Rise, and bake your Christ-mas bread: the
Rise, and light your Christ-mas fire; the
Rise, and o-pen wide the door; the

3. Rise, and bake your Christ-mas bread: Christ-ians, rise! The
5. Rise, and light your Christ-mas fire; Christ-ians, rise! The
7. Rise, and o-pen wide the door; Christ-ians, rise! The

world— is bare, And blank,— and dark— with
world— is old, And Time— is wea-ry, and
world— is wide, And ma-ny there be—— that

want and care, |
worn, and cold, } Yet Christ-mas comes in the morn-ing.
stand out-side, |

A Dutch melody, from *Souter Liedekens Ghemaect ter*
Eeren Gods, Antwerp, 1539, has been adapted to these words.

275

135 EARTHLY FRIENDS
(CHRISTMAS)

J. M. Neale

German, 16th century
(Geoffrey Shaw)

1. Earth-ly friends will change and fal-ter, Earth-ly hearts will va-ry:
He is born that can-not al-ter, Of the Vir-gin Ma-ry.

Born to-day, Raise the lay! Born to-day,— Twine the bay!

2. Je-sus Christ is born to suf-fer, Born for you, Born for you,

Hol-ly strew! 3. Je-sus Christ was born to con-quer, Born to save,

276

Born to save, Lau-rel wave! 4. Je-sus Christ was born to gov-ern,

Born a King, Born a King, Bay wreaths bring! 5. Je - sus Christ was

born of Ma - ry, Born for all. Well be - fall Hearth and hall!

Je - sus Christ was born at Christ - mas, Born for all.

Words written in 1853 by Dr. Neale for the melody in *Piae Cantiones* (cf. No. 141) of 'Omnis mundus jucundetur'. The tune is printed in Quentel, *Alte Catholische Geistliche Kirchengeseng*, 1599, the *Constanzer Gesangbuch*, 1600, and in many German books of the seventeenth century.

136 GOOD KING WENCESLAS

(ST. STEPHEN, 26 DECEMBER)

J. M. Neale

Piae Cantiones
(M. S.)

1. Good King Wen-ces - las looked out, On the Feast of Ste - phen,
2. 'Hi - ther, page, and stand by me, If thou know'st it, tell - ing,

When the snow lay round a - bout, Deep, and crisp, and ev - en:
Yon - der pea - sant, who is he? Where and what his dwell - ing?'

Bright-ly shone the moon that night, Though the frost was cru - el,
'Sire, he lives a good league hence, Un - der-neath the moun - tain,

When a poor man came in sight, Gath'-ring win-ter fu - el.
Right a - gainst the for - est fence, By Saint Ag - nes' foun - tain.'

3 'Bring me flesh, and bring me wine,
    Bring me pine-logs hither:
Thou and I will see him dine,
    When we bear them thither.'
Page and monarch, forth they went,
    Forth they went together;
Through the rude wind's wild lament
    And the bitter weather.

4 'Sire, the night is darker now,
    And the wind blows stronger;
Fails my heart, I know not how;
    I can go no longer.'
'Mark my footsteps, good my page;
    Tread thou in them boldly:
Thou shalt find the winter's rage
    Freeze thy blood less coldly.'

5 In his master's steps he trod,
    Where the snow lay dinted;
Heat was in the very sod
    Which the saint had printed.
Therefore, Christian men, be sure,
    Wealth or rank possessing,
Ye who now will bless the poor,
    Shall yourselves find blessing.

This rather confused narrative owes its popularity to the delightful tune, which is that of a Spring carol, 'Tempus adest floridum', No. 99. Unfortunately Neale in 1853 substituted for the Spring carol this 'Good King Wenceslas', one of his less happy pieces, which E. Duncan goes so far as to call 'doggerel', and Bullen condemns as 'poor and commonplace to the last degree'. The time has not yet come for a comprehensive book to discard it; but we reprint the tune in its proper setting ('Spring has now unwrapped the flowers'), not without hope that, with the present wealth of carols for Christmas, 'Good King Wenceslas' may gradually pass into disuse, and the tune be restored to spring-time. Neale did the same kind of thing to another Spring carol, 'In vernali tempore' (No. 98; cf. No. 102); but this was not popularized by Bramley & Stainer.

137 MASTERS IN THIS HALL
(CHRISTMAS)

William Morris

French
(arr. Gustav Holst)

Now - ell sing we clear! Holp - en are all folk on earth,— Born__ is God's Son so dear: Now - ell! Now - ell! Now - ell! Now - ell sing we loud! God to - day hath poor folk raised_ And__ cast a - down the proud.

(Men's voices only until last verse.   Last verse *Tutti*)

2. *Go - ing o'er the hills,____ Through the milk - white snow,____
4. *Quoth I, 'Fel - lows mine,____ Why this guise sit ye?____
6 *Quoth these fel - lows then,___ 'To Beth - lem town we go,____ To
8. Then to Beth - lem town____ We went two and two,____ And
10. And a lit - tle child____ On her arm had she,____
12. *This is Christ the Lord,____ Mas - ters, be ye glad!____

Heard I ewes___ bleat____ While the wind did blow:
Mak - ing but dull cheer,____ Shep - herds though ye be?'
see a might - y lord____ Lie in man - ger low':
in a sor - ry place____ Heard the ox - en low:
'Wot ye who this is?'____ Said the hinds to me:
Christ - mas is come in,____ And no folk should be sad:

Now - ell! Now - ell! Now - ell! Now - ell sing we clear! Holp - en

282

are all folk on earth,— Born— is God's Son so dear:

ff Tutti

Now - ell! Now - ell! Now - ell! Now - ell sing we loud! God to-

-day hath poor folk raised— And— cast a - down the proud.

The words were written for the old French carol tune shortly before 1860 by Morris, who was in Street's office with Edmund Sedding (architect and compiler of carols, brother of the more famous J. D. Sedding; he died early, in 1868). Sedding had obtained the tune from the organist at Chartres Cathedral, and he published the words and tune in his *Antient Christmas Carols*, 1860. The melody is here reharmonized. The starred verses can be omitted (the chorus gives the answer to v. 10); but a long carol is useful sometimes for processions, both in and out of church. This one should be popular with children. The characters can be distinguished in the singing, and the chorus sung by all.

138 O LITTLE TOWN
(CHRISTMAS EVE: CHRISTMAS)

Bishop Phillips Brooks

English traditional
(R.V.W.)

1. O lit - tle town of— Beth - le - hem, How still we— see thee— lie! Yet— in thy dark— streets shi - neth The ev - er - last - ing— light; The— hopes and fears of— all— the years Are met in— thee to - night.

A - bove thy deep and— dream - less sleep The si - lent stars go— by.

2. O morn - ing stars, to - ge - - - ther Pro - claim the ho - ly— birth, For— Christ is born— of— Ma - ry; And, gath - ered all— a - - bove, While— mor - tals sleep, the— ang - els— keep Their watch of— wond - 'ring love.

And prais - es sing to— God— the— King, And peace to— men on— earth;

284

3 How silently, how silently,
    The wondrous gift is given!
  So God imparts to human hearts
    The blessings of his heaven.
  No ear may hear his coming;
    But in this world of sin,
  Where meek souls will receive him, still
    The dear Christ enters in.

4 Where children pure and happy
    Pray to the blessèd child,
  Where misery cries out to thee,
    Son of the mother mild;
  Where charity stands watching
    And faith holds wide the door,
  The dark night wakes, the glory breaks,
    And Christmas comes once more.

5 O holy child of Bethlehem,
    Descend to us, we pray;
  Cast out our sin, and enter in,
    Be born in us to-day.
  We hear the Christmas angels
    The great glad tidings tell:
  O come to us, abide with us,
    Our Lord Emmanuel.

This hymn, with its tune ('The Ploughboy's Dream') from the *English Hymnal* (15),
and *Songs of Praise* (79), is so much a carol that we feel bound to include it in this book also.

139 INFINITE LIGHT
(EPIPHANY: LENT: GENERAL: MISSIONARY)

B. M. G.

English traditional
(M.S.)

SEMI-CHORUS

SOPRANO
ALTO

1. The great-ness of God in his love has been shown, The
2. He rolls the grim dark-ness and sor-row a-way, And

TENOR
BASS

light of his life on the na-tions is thrown; And
brings all our fears to the light of the day; The

that which the Jews and the Greeks did di-vine Is
i-dols are fall-en of an-ger and blood, And

CHORUS

come in the full-ness of Je-sus to shine: *The*
God is re-vealed as the lov-ing and good: *The*

Light of— the World— in— the— dark-ness has— shone, And—

grows— in— our— sight as— the— a - ges flow on.

3 And, though we have sinned like the prodigal son,
His love to our succour and welcome will run.
His gospel of pardon, of love and accord,
Will master oppression and shatter the sword:

The Light of the World etc.

4 The Light of the World is more clear to our sight
As errors disperse and men see him aright:
In lands long in shadow, his churches arise
And blaze for their neighbours the way of the wise:

The Light of the World etc.

This carol has been written to carry another traditional 'Virgin
unspotted' tune, which has been familiar for many years. Cf. Nos. 4 and 114.

140 THE BAND OF CHILDREN

(INNOCENTS' DAY: EPIPHANY TO LENT)

LAISSEZ PAITRE VOS BETES

(CHRISTMAS)

Frank Kendon

French
(M.S.)

Moderately quick

SOPRANO
ALTO

The stars shall light your jour-ney; Your mo-ther holds you

TENOR
BASS

close and warm; The don-key's pace shall rock you: Sleep, ba-by; dream no harm.

1. What songs_ are these,___ faint heard and far?___ The
2. What songs_ are these,___ faint heard and far?___ 'Tis

wind, may-be, in palm trees tall, Or run-ning stream, or night-bird's call; The
nei-ther wind in palm trees tall, Nor wa-ter-brook, nor night-bird's call, It

dark lies deep on de-sert, Where Jo-seph walked and Ma-ry rode, The
is the voice of child-ren Where Jo-seph walked and Ma-ry rode, The

dark lies deep on de - sert— Sleep well, thou child of God:
fierce wild beasts are friend - ly— Sleep well, thou child of God:

3 What forms are these, clear on the dark,
That shine, and yet are flesh and blood,
That laugh and sing along the road?
It is a crowd of children
Where Joseph walked and Mary rode,
A singing crowd of children—
Sleep well, thou child of God:

4 Never was seen so strange a guard:
About the footsore travellers they
In lovely circles moved, till day,
Until the baby wakened,
While Joseph trudged and Mary rode!
Such lullaby be all men's,
Sleep well, thou child of God:

LAISSEZ paître vos bêtes,
Pastoureaux, par monts et par vaux,
Laissez paître vos bêtes
Et venez chanter Nau.

J'ai ouï chanter le rossignol
Qui chantait un chant si nouveau,
Si haut, si beau,
Si resonneau,
Il me rompait la tête,
Tant il prêchait
Et caquetait.
A-donc prins ma houlette
Pour aller voir Naulet.

2 Je m'enquis au berger Naulet;
As-tu ouï le rossignolet
Tant joliet,
Qui gringotait
Là-haut sur une épine?
Oui, dit-il, oui,
Je l'ai ouï;
J'en ai pris ma buccine
Et m'en suis réjoui.

4 Sa mère avec lui se trouvait;
Un vieillard si leur éclairait.
Point à l'enfant
Ne ressemblant;
Il n'était pas son père,
Ce qu'au museau
J'aperçus tôt;
Il ressemble à sa mère,
Encore est-il plus beau.

3 Nous courûmes avec roideur
Pour voir notre doux rédempteur,
Et Créateur
Et formateur:
Il avait, Dieu le sçaiche,
Assez besoin
De plus de soin;
Il gisait dans la crèche
Sur un botteau de foin.

5 Or prions l'enfant, Roi du ciel
Qu'il nous donne à tous bon noël,
Et bonne paix
De nos méfaits,
Ne veuille avoir mémoire
De nos péchés,
Mais pardonner
A ceux du purgatoire
Et leurs maux soulager.

The words have been written for this tune, which is given as a 'noël ancien' by the Abbé Pellegrin (1663-1745) early in the eighteenth century, and is reprinted in the *Grande Bible des Noëls angevins* in 1766. The tune is still sung in the west of France to 'Laissez paître vos bêtes'; another and earlier carol, 'Laisse-qu'y tes affaires', is also associated with it. Roques prints yet another version, 'Venez, divin Messie'. The refrain may be sung at the end of each verse, as well as at the beginning.

141 JANUARY CAROL
(JANUARY AND FEBRUARY)

J. M. Neale

Piae Cantiones
(G.S.)

1. Earth to-day re - joi - ces,
   And ce - les - tial voi - ces,
2. Re - con-cil - i - a - tion,   Al - le - lu - ya, al - le - lu - ya,
   Glad-ness and sal - va - tion,
3. Though the cold grows strong-er,
   Yet the days grow long - er,

al - le - lu - ya,

(1.) Death can hurt_ no more;
     Tell that sin _ is o'er.
(2.) Peace that lasts_ for ay,
     Came on Christ-mas Day.
(3.) Though the world loves night;
     Christ is born_ our Light.

(1.) Da - vid's sling des - troys the foe: Sam - son lays the tem - ple low:
(2.) Gi - deon's fleece is wet with dew: So - lo - mon is crowned a - new:
(3.) Now the di - al's type is learnt: Burns the bush that is not burnt:

War— and strife— are done; God and man are— one.

Written by Dr. Neale in 1853 for the tune 'Ave maris stella lucens' in *Piae Cantiones* (1582).

The now famous *Piae Cantiones* was compiled by Theodoricus Petrus of Nyland in Finland, in 1582, when he was a student at Rostock near Lübeck: he was still alive in 1625. The songs spread in the reformed Church of Sweden and Finland, and were still sung in Swedish schools in 1700, and in Finland late in the nineteenth century. Peter of Nyland's *Piae Cantiones* (perhaps the unique copy) was brought over by the British Minister at Stockholm, who gave it to Dr. Neale, c. 1852. Neale gave it to Helmore; and together they published from it *Carols for Christmastide* (1853) and *Carols for Eastertide* (1854), from which collections Neale's carols are taken. An edition of *Piae Cantiones* (altered) was published by Dr. G. R. Woodward in 1910. The original copy is now in the British Museum. See preface.

142 CHILDREN'S SONG OF THE NATIVITY

Frances Chesterton

English traditional
(R.V.W.)

This folk-tune 'Stowey' appears in *Songs of Praise* (377) where it is set to other words.

143 THE WORLD'S DESIRE
(NATIVITY)

G. K. Chesterton

Traditional
(M.S.)

1. The Christ-child lay on Mary's lap, His hair was like a light. (O weary, weary, were the world, But here is all aright.) 2. The Christ-child lay on Mary's breast, His hair was like a star. (O stern and cunning are the kings, But here the true hearts are.)

3. The Christ-child lay on Mary's heart, His hair was like a fire. (O weary, weary, is the world, But here the world's desire.) 4. The Christ-child stood at Mary's knee, His hair was like a crown, And all the flowers looked up at him And all the stars looked down.

Set to a tune kindly communicated by the
Rev. J. R. Van Pelt, Theological Seminary, Atlanta, Georgia, U.S.A.

144 WHITE LENT
(ASH WEDNESDAY TO THE EVE OF PASSION SUNDAY)
QUITTEZ, PASTEURS
(CHRISTMAS)

L.M.

Angevin
(M.S.)

Sopranos and altos sing the words.   Tenors and basses hum the accompaniment.

In moderate time

SOPRANO
ALTO

1. Now quit your care And an-xious fear and wor-ry; For
2. Lent comes in the spring, And spring is pied with bright-ness; The

TENOR
BASS

schemes are vain And frett-ing brings no gain. To prayer, to
sweet-est flowers, Keen winds, and sun, and showers, Their health do

prayer! Bells call and clash and hur-ry, In Lent the bells do cry, 'Come
bring To make Lent's chas-tened white-ness; For life to men brings light And

buy,— come buy,— Come buy with love the love most high, Come
might,— and might,— And might to those whose hearts are right, And

buy,— come buy,— Come buy with love the love most high!'
might,— and might,— And might to those whose hearts are right.

3 To bow the head
  In sackcloth and in ashes,
    ' * Or rend the soul,
      Such grief is not Lent's goal;
  But to be led
    To where God's glory flashes,
      His beauty to come nigh,
        To fly, to fly,
          To fly where truth and light do lie.

4 For is not this
  The fast that I have chosen?—
    The prophet spoke—
      To shatter every yoke,
  Of wickedness
    The grievous bands to loosen,
      Oppression put to flight,
        To fight, to fight,
          To fight till every wrong's set right.

5 For righteousness
  And peace will show their faces
    To those who feed
      The hungry in their need,
  And wrongs redress,
    Who build the old waste places,
      And in the darkness shine.
        Divine, divine,
          Divine it is when all combine!

6 Then shall your light
  Break forth as doth the morning;
    Your health shall spring,
      The friends you make shall bring
  God's glory bright,
    Your way through life adorning;
      And love shall be the prize.
        Arise, arise,
          Arise! and make a paradise!

Rather quick

The last verse and any other selected verses. (All sing the words)

S.
A.
6. Then shall your light Break forth as doth the morn-ing; Your health shall spring, The

T.
B.

friends you make shall bring God's glo-ry bright, Your way through life a-dorn-ing; And

A-rise, a-rise, A-rise! and make a par-a--

love shall be the prize. A-rise, a-rise, A-rise, a-rise, a-

A-rise! and make a par-a-

-dise! A-rise, a-rise,

-rise, a-rise, A-rise, a-rise, A-rise! and make a par-a-dise!

-dise! For French words and footnote see overleaf.

* *Or to afflict the soul,* in some editions   295

QUITTEZ, pasteurs,
  Vos brebis, vos houlettes,
    Votre hameau
    Et le soin du troupeau;
Changez vos pleurs
  En une joie parfaite;
    Allez tous adorer
      Un Dieu, un Dieu,
    Un Dieu qui vient vous consoler.

2 Vous le verrez
  Couché dans une étable
    Comme un enfant
    Nu, pauvre, languissant;
Reconnaissez
  Son amour ineffable
    Pour nous venir chercher
      Il est, il est,
    Il est le fidèle berger!

3 Rois d'Orient
  L'étoile vous éclaire;
    A ce grand roi
    Rendez hommage et foi.
L'astre brillant
  Vous mène à la lumière
    De ce soleil naissant;
      Offrez, offrez,
    Offrez l'or, la myrrhe et l'encens.

4 Esprit divin
  A qui tout est possible
    Percez nos coeurs
    De vos douces ardeurs;
Notre destin
  Par vous devient paisible;
    Dieu prétend nous donner
      Le ciel, le ciel,
    Le ciel en venant s'incarner.

The English words are in part a paraphrase of the Lent Lesson, Isaiah lviii. The tune is printed in L. Roques, *Noëls Anciens* (nineteenth century, undated); there is a slightly different version in L. Eugène Grimault, *Noëls Angevins*, 1878.

145 MOTHERING SUNDAY
(MID-LENT)
ICH WEISS EIN LIEBLICH ENGELSPIEL
(GENERAL)

George Hare Leonard

German, 14th century
(M.S.)

Sopranos sing words, other parts hum accompaniment

1. It is the day of all the year, Of all the year the one day, When
2. So I'll put on my Sun-day coat, And in my hat a fea-ther, And

A.T.B. hum

I shall see my mo-ther dear And bring her cheer, A - mo-ther-ing on Sun- day.
get the lines I writ by rote, With many a note, That I've a-strung to - ge - ther.

3 And now to fetch my wheaten cake,
To fetch it from the baker,
He promised me, for mother's sake,
The best he'd bake
For me to fetch and take her.

4 Well have I known, as I went by
One hollow lane, that none day
I'd fail to find—for all they're shy—
Where violets lie,
As I went home on Sunday.

5 *My sister Jane is waiting-maid
Along with Squire's lady;
And year by year her part she's played,
And home she stayed,
To get the dinner ready.

6 *For mother'll come to church, you'll see—
Of all the year it's the day—
'The one,' she'll say, 'that's made for me.'
And so it be:
It's every mother's free day.

7 *The boys will all come home from town,
Not one will miss that one day;
And every maid will bustle down
To show her gown,
A-mothering on Sunday.

8 It is the day of all the year,
Of all the year the one day;
And here come I, my mother dear,
To bring you cheer,
A-mothering on Sunday.

For alternative harmonizations see overleaf.

297

FAUX BOURDON Version (for choice of verses)
Tenors sing words, other parts hum accompaniment

Iᴛ is the day of all the year,
Of all the year the one day,
When I shall see my mother dear
And bring her cheer,
A-mothering on Sunday.

2 So I'll put on my Sunday coat,
And in my hat a feather,
And get the lines I writ by rote,
With many a note,
That I've a-strung together.

3 And now to fetch my wheaten cake,
To fetch it from the baker,
He promised me, for mother's sake,
The best he'd bake
For me to fetch and take her.

4 Well have I known, as I went by
One hollow lane, that none day
I'd fail to find—for all they're shy—
Where violets lie,
As I went home on Sunday.

5 *My sister Jane is waiting-maid
Along with Squire's lady;
And year by year her part she's played,
And home she stayed,
To get the dinner ready.

6 *For mother'll come to church, you'll see—
Of all the year it's the day—
'The one,' she'll say, 'that's made for me.'
And so it be:
It's every mother's free day.

7 *The boys will all come home from town,
Not one will miss that one day;
And every maid will bustle down
To show her gown,
A-mothering on Sunday.

8 It is the day of all the year,
Of all the year the one day;
And here come I, my mother dear,
To bring you cheer,
A-mothering on Sunday.

For LAST VERSE all sing words

8. It is the day of all the year, Of all the year the one day; And here come I, my mo-ther dear, To bring you cheer, A - mo-ther-ing on Sun-day.

ICH weiss ein lieblich Engelspiel
Da ist all's Leid zergangen:
Im Himmelreich ist Freuden viel
Ohn' Endes Ziel;
Dahin soll uns verlangen.

2 Weil Gott uns durch die Gnade sein
Wollt lieblich dahin weisen,
So steh' auf, edle Seele mein,
Und walle herein
Sein Lob sollst ewig preisen.

3 Gott spricht: Nun leb' in Seeligkeit;
Von dir will ich nicht scheiden.
Dies Reich hab' ich dich zubereit
Von Ewigkeit
In Wonn und allen Freuden.

Heinrich von Laufenberg, 1421

'He who goes a-mothering finds violets in the lane.' In many parts of the country it was the custom for the children of the family who had left the old home to come back to visit their mother on the 4th Sunday in Lent (Mid-Lent Sunday). The eldest son would bring a wheaten cake—in modern times a plum cake with an icing of sugar, or a simnel-cake. Sometimes cinnamon comfits ('lambs'-tails'), or little white sugar-plums with a carraway seed, or some morsel of spice, within—such as may still be found at country fairs—were brought for an offering. One of the children home for the day would stay in and mind the house, so that the mother should be free for once to attend morning service at the church.

A folk-tune of the fourteenth century, made into a carol ('Ich weiss ein lieblich Engelspiel'), c. 1450. In a fifteenth-century Strassburg MS. (which was burnt in the war of 1870), printed by Wackernagel and others.

A translation of the artless German words is given below (and may be sung when a carol of more general character is wanted):

I know a lovely angel-game,
    Where sorrow has its ending;
And heaven is there with joy aflame,
And endless fame:
    'Tis there we would be wending.

2 May God through his abounding grace
    Us there in love be leading!
Now stand up, noble soul, and face
That happy place
    To which thou would'st be speeding!

3 Then God a ring from off his hand
    Will place upon thy finger,
And pledge thee,—' 'Mid this happy band
Within this land
    For ever shalt thou linger.'

146 THE MERCHANTS' CAROL
(PALM SUNDAY: HOLY WEEK)

Frank Kendon

English traditional
(M.S.)

SOPRANO
ALTO

TENOR
BASS

Rather quick

1. As we rode down the steep hill-side, Twelve mer-chants with our
2. Be-neath the o-lives fast we rode, And lou-der came the

fair — — ing, A shout a-cross the hol — low land Came
shout — — ing: 'So great a noise must mean,' said we, 'A

loud up-on our hear — — ing, A shout, a song, a
king, be-yond all doubt — — ing!' Spurred on, did we, this

thou — sand strong, A thou-sand lus-ty voi — ces: 'Make
king to see, And left the mules to fol — low; And

haste,' said I, I knew not why, 'Je - ru - sa - lem re - joi - ces!'
near - er, clear - er rang the noise A - long the Ki - dron hol - low.

3 Behold, a many-coloured crowd
About the gate we found there;
But one among them all, we marked,
One man who made no sound there;
Still louder ever rose the crowd's
'Hosanna in the highest!'
'O King,' thought I, 'I know not why
In all this joy thou sighest.'

4 *A Merchant:*
'Then he looked up, he looked at me;

But whether he spoke I doubted:
How could I hear so calm a speech
While all the rabble shouted?
And yet these words, it seems, I heard:
"I shall be crowned tomorrow."
They struck my heart with sudden smart,
And filled my bones with sorrow.'

5 We followed far, we traded not,
But long we could not find him.
The very folk that called him king
Let robbers go and bind him.
We found him then, the sport of men,
Still calm among their crying;
And well we knew his words were true—
He was most kingly dying.

The words written for the traditional tune, which we have distinguished by the name of 'Golden'; cf. Nos. 165 and 173. It can also be sung to the words of No. 165.

301

147 EASTER CAROL
(EASTER)
NOUS ALLONS, MA MIE
(CHRISTMAS)

N.S.T.

French
(M.S.)

Moderately quick

1. Cheer_ up, friends and neigh - bours, Now_ it's East - er - tide;
2. Out_ from snow-drifts chill - y, Roused from drow-sy_ hours,

Stop_ from end - less la - bours, Wor - ries put a - side:
Blue - bell wakes, and li - ly; God_ calls up the_ flowers!

Men_ should rise from sad - ness, E - vil, fol - ly,_ strife,
In - - to life he rais - es All_ the sleep - ing_ buds;

When_ God's might - y glad - ness Brings_ the earth to_ life.
Mea - dows weave his prais - es, And_ the spang - led_ woods.

3 All his truth and beauty,
   All his righteousness,
Are our joy and duty,
   Bearing his impress:
Look! the earth waits breathless
   After winter's strife:
Easter shows man deathless,
   Spring leads death to life.

4 Ours the more and less is;
   But, changeless all the days,
God revives and blesses,
   Like the sunlight rays.
'All mankind is risen,'
   The Easter bells do ring,
While from out their prison
   Creep the flowers of spring!

NOUS allons, ma mie,
   Voir un nouveau-né;
C'est notre Messie
   Qui nous est donné:
Nous verrons la mère
   De ce bel enfant,
Nous verrons le père—
   Ah, que Dieu est grand!

2 Dieu, quelle nouvelle!
   Qu'est-ce que j'entends!
Le croyant fidèle
   Sait bien qu'en ce temps
Nous verrons paraître
   Le Sauveur promis.
Il vient donc de naître,
   Cet aimable fils.

3 Allons, mes compagnes,
   Voir le fils de Dieu.
Est-ce en ces campagnes,
   Autour de ce lieu
Qu'il a pris naissance?
   Quels sont ses parents?
Ayons connaissance
   De ces bonnes gens.

4 Ne soyez en peine
   De savoir ce lieu;
C'est en cette plaine
   Que le fils de Dieu
Pour nous vient de naître:
   O bienheureux jour
Qui voit notre maître
   Bénir ce séjour!

Words written for the French carol tune,
'Nous allons, ma mie', printed by Grimault, Roques, and others.

148 CHRIST THE LORD IS RISEN

(EASTER)

I. Watts (1709)

German
(arr. Geoffrey Shaw)

SOPRANO ALTO

1. Christ the Lord is ri - sen! Now
2. Christ the Lord is ri - sen! 'Twas
3. Christ the Lord is ri - sen! Re-

TENOR BASS

is the hour of dark - ness past; Christ
by thy blood, im - mor - tal Lamb, Thine
-joice, ye heavens! let ev - 'ry star Shine

hath as - sumed his reign - ing power. Bear - mies trod the temp - ter down; 'Twas
with new glo - ries round the sky! Saints,

-hold — the great — ac - cus - er cast Down
by — thy word — and power - ful name They
while — ye sing — the heav'n - ly war, Raise

from — the skies, to rise — no more:⟩
gained — the bat - tle and — re - nown:⟩ Al -
your — Re - deem - er's name — on high!⟩

-le - - lu - ya, — al - le - - lu - ya.

Verses by Isaac Watts (1674-1748), with refrains added, to fit an old
German melody reprinted in the *Gesang- und Gebetbuch für die Diöcese Trier*, 1871.

149 LOVE IS COME AGAIN

(EASTER)
NOEL NOUVELET
(CHRISTMAS)

J. M. C. Crum

French
(M.S.)

In moderate time

SOPRANO
ALTO

1. Now the green blade ris - eth from the bur - ied grain,
2. In the grave they laid him, Love whom men had slain,

TENOR
BASS

Wheat_ that in dark_ earth_ ma - ny_ days has lain;
Think - ing that nev - er_ he would wake a - gain,

Love lives a - gain, that with the dead has been:
Laid in the earth like grain that sleeps un - seen:

Love is come a - gain, Like wheat that_spring - eth green.
Love is come a - gain, Like wheat that_spring - eth green.

3 Forth he came at Easter, like the risen grain,
He that for three days in the grave had lain,
Quick from the dead my risen Lord is seen:

Love is come again, etc.

4 When our hearts are wintry, grieving, or in pain,
Thy touch can call us back to life again,
Fields of our hearts that dead and bare have been:

Love is come again, etc.

NOEL nouvelet, Noël chantons ici.
Dévotes gens, crions à Dieu merci!
Chantons Noël pour le roi nouvelet.

Noël nouvelet, Noël chantons ici.

2 L'ange disait; pasteurs, partez d'ici
L'âme en repos et le coeur réjoui;
En Bethléem trouverez l'agnelet;

Noël nouvelet, etc.

3 En Bethléem, étant tous réunis,
Trouvent l'enfant, Joseph, Marie aussi.
La crèche était au lieu d'un bercelet,

Noël nouvelet, etc.

4 Bientôt les rois, par l'étoile éclaircis
De l'orient dont ils étaient sortis
A Bethléem vinrent un matinet.

Noël nouvelet, etc.

5 L'un portait l'or, l'autre l'encens béni;
Un autre encore à Jésus myrrhe offrit.
L'étable alors au paradis semblait.

Noël nouvelet, etc.

6 Voici mon Dieu, mon Sauveur Jésus-Christ,
Par qui sera le prodige accompli
De nous sauver par son sang vermeillet!

Noël nouvelet, etc.

Words written for the old French tune associated with 'Noël nouvelet'.

150 THE WORLD ITSELF
(EASTER)

J. M. Neale

Piae Cantiones
(G.S.)

1. The world it-self keeps Eas-ter Day, And
2. There stood three Ma-ries by the tomb, On

Eas-ter larks are sing - ing; And Eas - ter flowers are
Eas-ter morn-ing ear - ly; When day had scarce - ly

bloom-ing gay, And Eas-ter buds are spring-ing: Al - le - lu - ya, al -
chased the gloom, And dew was white and pearl - y: Al - le - lu - ya, al -

-le - lu - ya: The Lord of all things lives a - new, And all his works are
-le - lu - ya: With lov - ing but with err - ing mind, They came the Prince of

ris - ing too: Ho - san - na in ex - cel - - sis.
life__ to find: Ho - san - na in ex - cel - - sis.

3 But earlier still the angel sped,
   His news of comfort giving;
And 'Why', he said, 'among the dead
   Thus seek ye for the Living?'
      Alleluya, alleluya:
'Go, tell them all, and make them blest;
Tell Peter first, and then the rest':

Hosanna etc.

4 But one, and one alone remained
   With love that could not vary;
And thus a joy past joy she gained,
   That sometime sinner, Mary,
      Alleluya, alleluya:
The first the dear, dear form to see
Of him that hung upon the tree:

Hosanna etc.

5 The world itself keeps Easter Day,
   Saint Joseph's star is beaming,
Saint Alice has her primrose gay,
   Saint George's bells are gleaming:
      Alleluya, alleluya:
The Lord hath risen, as all things tell:
Good Christians, see ye rise as well!

Hosanna etc.

The words were written by Neale (*Carols for Eastertide,* 1854) for the tune 'O Christe, rex piissime'
in *Piae Cantiones* (cf. No. 141) with the Alleluyas repeated for the concluding refrain. As this does
not fit the melody, 'Hosanna in excelsis' has been substituted.

151 ATHENS
(EASTER)

J. M. Neale

Piae Cantiones
(Geoffrey Shaw)

1. 'Twas a-bout the dead of night, And Ath-ens_ lay in
Moon-light on the tem-ples slept, And touched the_rocks with

2. Met were they to hear and judge The teach-ing_ of a
O'er the o-cean he had come, Through want, and toil, and

slum - - ber;
um - - ber; (1.) And the Court of Mars were met In

stran - - ger;
dan - - ger; (2.) And he wor-shipped for his God One

grave and rev-er-end num - - ber:
cra - dled in a man - - ger: *Ev - er - more and*

ev - er - more, Christ - ians, sing_ al - le - lu - - ya.

3 While he spake against their gods,
  And temples' vain erection,
Patiently they gave him ear,
  And granted him protection;
Till with bolder voice and mien
  He preached the resurrection:

  Evermore etc.

4 Some they scoffed, and some they
    spake
  Of blasphemy and treason;
Some replied with laughter loud,
  And some replied with reason;
Others put it off until
  A more convenient season:

  Evermore etc.

5 Athens heard and scorned it then,
  Now Europe hath received it,
Wise men mocked and jeered it once,
  Now children have believed it;
This, good Christians, was the day
  That gloriously achieved it:

  Evermore etc.

Written by Neale in 1853 for a tune ('Scribere proposui') in *Piae Cantiones* (cf. No. 141).

152 FESTIVAL CAROL
(EASTER TO TRINITY SUNDAY, ETC.)

S. P.

Dutch
(Geoffrey Shaw)

1. How great the har - vest is_____ Of him who came to
The hearts of men are his,_____ Our law the love he
2. And though the news did seem_____ Too good for man's be-
'Tis not an emp - ty dream_____ Too high for our a-

save_____ us!
gave_____ us. (1.) The world lay cru - el,
-liev - - - - - - - ing, (2.) He tri - umphed in__ the
-chiev - - - - - - - ing.

blind, Nought hold - ing, nought di - vin - - ing; He came to hu - man
strife, O'er all his foes he tow - - ered; They killed the Prince of__

kind, And now the light is shi - ning, is shi - ning, is
life, But he hath death o'er - pow - ered, o'er - pow - ered, o'er-

312

shi - ning, is shi - - - - - - ning.
-pow - ered, o'er - pow - - - - - ered.

3 Then came the Father's call;
    His work on earth was ended;
That he might light on all,
    To heaven the Lord ascended.
To heaven so near to earth,
    Our hearts we do surrender:
There all things find their worth
    And human life its splendour, its splendour.

4 The power by which there came
    The Word of God among us
Was love's eternal flame,
    Whose light and heat are flung us;
That Spirit sent from God,
    Within our hearts abiding,
Hath brought us on our road
    And still the world is guiding, is guiding.

5 In Three made manifest,
    Thou source of all our being,
Thou loveliest, truest, best,
    Beyond our power of seeing;
Thou power of light and love,
    Thou life that never diest—
To thee in whom all move
    Be glory in the highest, the highest!

Words written for the Dutch tune, 'De Liefde Voortgebracht', a very popular song in the seventeenth century, which was set to 'Hoe groot de Vruechten zijn' in the Amsterdam Psalter of J. Oudaen.

153 SONG OF THE SPIRIT
(WHITSUNTIDE, ETC.)

O. B.C.

Dutch
(M.S.)

SOLO

Now sing we of the Par-a-clete, The Light, the Beam of God, to greet.

CHORUS

SOPRANO
ALTO

1. When Christ blessed his dis - ci - ples, 'Ye are my friends,' he
2. Long af - ter, rose a pro - phet Who hailed the Spi - rit's

TENOR
BASS

said, 'Let not your heart be trou - bled, And be ye not a -
day, And said, 'Men first in ter - ror As slaves did God o -

Bass
(1.) 'Let not your heart be trou - bled, And be ye not a -
(2.) And said, 'Men first in ter - ror As slaves did God o -

-fraid; When he the Breath of Truth is come, To all the truth he'll
- bey. Then came the age when man as son Could serve, and so God's

Tenor
(1.) When he is come, To
(2.) Then came the age, Could
(3.) The power of fraud, Vain
(4.) He sci - ence finds, And

-fraid; When he the Breath of Truth is come, To all the truth he'll
- bey. Then came the age when man as son Could serve, and so God's

314

bring you home, Tho' now ye can-not bear it.' So spoke he un-to
grace be won: A third—and we are near it— Will be of love, all

all the truth, tho' now ye can-not bear it.' (1.) So spoke he un-to
serve, and so, a third—and we are near it—(2.) Will be of love, all
forms, and fear, love's crown is ours to wear it;
he the light, and his the he-ro's mer-it;

bring you home, Tho' now ye can-not bear it.' So
grace be won: A third—and we are near it— Will

And prom-ised us the Spi - - rit._____
The free - dom of the Spi - - rit.'_____

Christ - en - dom,_____
blind - ness gone,_____

And prom-ised us the Spi - rit.
The free-dom of the Spi - rit.'

3 From slavery and childhood
  Man grows to noble youth,
And free the Spirit makes us
  To follow after truth:
The power of fraud, and dull pretence,
Vain forms, and fear, is banished hence;
  Love's crown is ours to wear it;
Through all our faithless impotence
  The light shines from the Spirit.

4 Brave thinkers saw the vision,
  The story poets wove,
Of truth and grace unhindered,
  The eternal Spirit's love:
For he the knowledge science finds,
And he the light in artists' minds,
  And his the hero's merit;
All lovely things of all the kinds
  Are planets of the Spirit.

The words have been written for an old Dutch carol tune, given by J. A. Thijm to E. Sedding, who published it in England in 1864. The reference in v. 2 is to the twelfth-century mystic, Joachim of Floris, Dante's:

Il Calavrese abate Giovacchino
Di spirito profetico dotato,

(*Paradiso*, xii) who was the precursor of Francis of Assisi.

154 THE SPIRIT
(WHITSUNTIDE: GENERAL)
COURONS A LA FETE
(CHRISTMAS)

Geoffrey Dearmer

Angevin
(M.S.)

In moderate time

SOPRANO
ALTO

1. Winds of God un - fail - ing fill the sun - lit sails Of a
2. If ye then per - ceive and if the heart de - sire, Shall the

TENOR
BASS

great ship sail - ing where con - jec - ture fails: Seek - ers
mind a - chieve, and spi - rit shall as - pire; Then shall

Seek - ers
Then shall

we, and we must dis - co - ver, Doubt we not tho' the chart is hid— Chart we
man see him, and shall praise him In the fern, in the sea and cloud; Ev - 'ry

we,   seek - ers we,   Doubt we not,   doubt we not.
man,   then shall man,   In the fern,   in the fern,

may not see, Plot - ted by the world's great Lo - ver Down in
flower and tree In the sap of life must raise him, As in

316

Ga - li - lee; Cap - tain, Prince and Pi - lot he.
Ga - li - lee In the form of man rose he.

3 His is each profession, every man his priest
Who in work's expression finds his joy increased:
In his church are the ploughman, sailor,
Merchant, prince, artisan, and clerk,
  All whoe'er they be,
Craftsman, thinker, tinker, tailor,
  Come to Galilee,
Find a plan, and that is he.

4 Those who love him wholly need not him confess,
Since their lives must solely him in them express;
He's the goal that man ever searches,
How should man see that goal afar?
  Each in his degree
That doth love him, of his church is.
  Down in Galilee
Founder of our church was he.

Courons à la fête, ne différons pas,
Que chacun s'apprête à suivre mes pas.
Venez donc, bergers, bergères,
Hâtez-vous, redoublez vos pas!
  Un Dieu plein d'appas
Mérite que l'on s'empresse;
  Un Dieu plein d'appas
Vient nous sauver du trépas.

2 Quittons nos houlettes, laissons nos troupeaux,
Prenons nos musettes et nos chalumeaux,
Pour chanter mille chansonnettes,
Pour jouer nos beaux airs nouveaux,
  Oublions nos maux,
Ne craignons plus la disette;
  Le fils du Très-Haut
Nous donnera ce qu'il faut.

3 Cet enfant aimable et plein de douceur
Demande en partage l'amour de nos coeurs.
Offrons-lui d'un amour sincère,
Aimons-bien ce doux rédempteur;
  Ce divin sauveur
Prend pitié de nos misères;
  Ce divin sauveur
Vient nous combler de bonheur.

4 Il voit notre crime et sa charité
Le rend la victime d'un père irrité.
Quel excès d'amour le plus tendre!
Nos péchés nous sont effacés;
  Cessons de pleurer.
Réjouis-toi, berger Sylvandre;
  Cessons de pleurer,
Oublions nos maux passés.

Words written for the melody 'Courons à la fête', in the *Grande Bible des Noëls Angevins*, 1766, republished by Grimault in 1878. Cf. Legeay, *Noëls Anciens*, 1875.

155 APRIL

Geoffrey Dearmer

Welsh
(M.S.)

Rather quick

SOPRANO
ALTO

1. Now A-pril has come, The coun-try grows sweet here, The chiff-chaff and
2. A touch of her wand— The buds rise to meet her, And birds' eyes all

TENOR
BASS

wheat - ear, Be - hold, from the land of ripe o - ran - ges come! And
greet her— Why ev - en the gar - ru - lous ducks on the pond See

cher - ry and plum, With white blos - som gleam - ing, The hill - sides are
signs of her wand! As if the Ma - gi - cian Sent ducks on a

seam - ing. Too long have been dumb The woods and the wold: With
miss - ion With news from be - yond, With ti - dings which they Through

318

Words written for the Welsh traditional carol tune, 'Hir Oes i Fair'

156 SUMMER TIME
(SUMMER)
UNE VAINE CRAINTE
(CHRISTMAS)

Rose Fyleman

French
(M.S.)

Moderately quick

SOPRANO
ALTO

1. Lift your hid - den fa - ces Ye who wept and prayed;
2. Now from mead and spin - ney Now from flood and foam,
3. Fa - thers, leave your la - bours, Sons, be glad and gay;

TENOR
BASS

Leave your cov - ert pla - ces Ye who were a - fraid. Here's a gold - en
Feath-ered, furred and fin - ny, All ye crea-tures come. Here ye shall dis-
Tell your friends and neigh - bours Of our ho - ly - day. Joy - ful - ly fore-

sto - ry, Here is sil - ver news, Here be gifts of glo - ry
-cov - er That for which ye wait; Win - ter days are ov - er,—
-gath - er, Sor - row now is done: We have found a Fa - ther,

For all men to choose:
Sing and cel - e - brate! *Al - le - lu - ya, al - le - lu - ya, praise the*
We have found a Son:

Lord with thanks - giv - ing: prais - es sing to God.

UNE vaine crainte trouble vos esprits.
L'âme en est atteinte, vous êtes surpris;
Chassez la tristesse qui règne en ces lieux
Que votre allégresse vole jusqu'aux cieux.
  Alleluya, alleluya
  Kyrie, Christe, Kyrie eleison.

2 La bonne nouvelle vient en ce grand jour,
  Cher peuple fidèle, chercher ton amour.
  C'est Dieu qui m'envoie ici t'annoncer
  La plus grande joie qui puisse arriver.
    Alleluya, etc.

3 Prêtez donc l'oreille attentivement
  A cette merveille, car en ce moment
  Une vierge mère vous donne le fils
  Dont Dieu est le père, Oui, je vous le dis.
    Alleluya, etc.

4 Rendez-lui visite, redoublez le pas,
  Allez donc bien vite et ne craignez pas.
  De vos bergeries, s'il en est besoin,
  Et de ces prairies nous prendrons le soin.
    Alleluya, etc.

5 Ce maître des Anges, Dieu de majesté,
  Dans de pauvres langes est emmailloté.
  C'est là le Messie, roi de l'univers,
  Qui vous rend la vie en brisant vos fers.
    Alleluya, etc.

Based on the French carol, 'Une vaine crainte', with last part of the refrain from Ps. 147. Roques prints the melody, and also Grimault (to the words 'Grâce soit rendue') who says there are many variants in Champagne, Burgundy, and Anjou.

  Summer carols seem to have been more common in Wales than in England. Hone, analysing the *Blodeugerdd Cymru*, an Anthology for Wales, in his *Ancient Mysteries*, at the beginning of the nineteenth century, says that it contains '48 Christmas carols, 9 summer carols, 3 May carols, one winter carol, one nightingale carol, and a carol to Cupid'.

157 SUMMER CAROL

Geoffrey Dearmer

Béarnais
(M.S.)

In moderate time

1. The dawn-wind now is wak - ing, Round go the wind-mill's
2. Now quick - ly goes the grey light; A - slant, the sun re -
3. Bright flowers the woods a - dorn - ing Show earth's no long-er

arms, And sun on sha-dow break - ing Lights up the shel-tered
-deems A whole long day of day - light; Gold crown a wealth of
blind, As once on Christ-mas morn - ing, When snow the world did

farms.___ Un - der cows the milk-maids crouch-ing In the
beams.___ Chick-ens flut - ter, strut and bab - ble; Run-ning
bind, ___ When the shep - herds and the sa - ges And the

mists   of   morn - ing   grow;——   Boys with   hea - vy   hor - ses
ducks   the   duck-ponds   fill; ——   Ear - ly   breez - es   bear the
kings   first   met their   King,——   Brought him   wis - dom,   wealth, and

slouch - ing   Down to   wa - ter   lum - ber   slow;——   Grey as
gab - ble,   And the   light   in - creas - es   till——   Soon it
wag - es,   Though he   was   the   lit - tlest   thing;——   Sud - den-

rocks the strag - gling sha-dowy flocks With   si - lent shep - herds go.
finds be - yond   the   rab - ble   The black-bird's yel - low bill.
-ly the   ir - on   ag - es   Had yield-ed to   the spring.

Written for the Béarnais carol-tune, 'Haut! haut!
Pierrot', printed by P. Darricades, in *Noëls Béarnais*, 1877.

158 THANKSGIVING CAROL

(HARVEST: AUTUMN)

Eleanor Farjeon

German, 15th century
(Geoffrey Shaw)

1. Fields of corn, give up your ears, Now your ears are hea - vy,
Wheat and oats and bar - ley - spears, All your har - vest - le - vy.

2. Vines, send in your bunch of grapes, Now the bunch is clus - tered,
Be your gold and pur - ple shapes Round the al - tar mus - tered.

3. Gar - den, give your gay - est flowers, Hedge, your wild - est bring - in,
Turn the church - es in - to bowers Lit - tle birds shall sing _ in.

(1.) Where your sheaves of plen - ty lean, Men once more the
(2.) Where the hang - ing bunch - es shine Men once more shall
(3.) Where the child - ren sing their glee Men once more the

grain shall glean Of the Ev - er - Liv - ing,
taste the wine Of the Ev - er - Liv - ing,
Flower shall see Of the Ev - er - Liv - ing,

God the Lord will bless the field, — Bring - ing in its
God the Lord will bless the root, — Bring - ing in its
God the Lord will bless the throng, — Lift - ing up its

au - tumn yield Glad - ly to Thanks - giv - - ing.
au - tumn fruit Glad - ly to Thanks - giv - - ing.
au - tumn song Glad - ly in Thanks - giv - - ing.

Words based upon 'Der Tag der ist so freudenreich'; with melody in M. Vehe's *Gesangbuch*, 1537, Strassburg, *Gros-Kirchengesangbuch*, 1560, Corner, 1631, &c. A melody, says Riemann, at latest of the fifteenth century; set by J. S. Bach in the eighteenth century. Mone gives the Latin words ('Dies est laetitiae) from a fifteenth-century MS.; but there are many versions of the German words, and several melodies are given by Baümker.
Neale's version 'Royal day that chasest gloom' also appears in the *Cowley Carol Book*.

325

159 GOLDEN SHEAVES
(HARVEST)

J. S. B. Monsell

Basque
(M.S.)

sea - - sons In fruit - ful or - der move, Sing
full - - ness All things with large— in - crease, He
-fore him When at his feet— ye fall, And

to the Lord of har - vest A song of hap - py love.
crowns the year with good - ness, With plen - ty and with peace.
with your lives a - dore— him, Who gave his life for all.

C♯ for last verse

Monsell's words set to 'Khanta zagun', as given in C. Bordes,
Archives de la Tradition Basque, and *Noëls Basques Anciens*, 1897.

160 ANGELS HOLY
(GENERAL: PRAISE)

John Stuart Blackie

Flemish
(M.S.)

In moderate time

1. An - gels ho - ly, high_ and_ low - ly, Sing the prais - es of_ the_ Lord; Earth and sky, all liv - ing na - ture, Star - ry tem - ples a - zure-floored, Man, the stamp of thy_ Cre - a - tor, Praise ye, praise ye, God_ the_ Lord:

2. O - cean hoar - y, tell_ his_ glo - ry, Cliffs, where tum - bling seas_ have_ roared, Might - y moun - tains, pur - ple - breast - ed, Crag where ea - gle's pride hath soared, Peaks cloud - cleav - ing, snow - y - crest - ed, Praise ye, praise ye, God_ the_ Lord:

Praise ye, praise ye, God the Lord, Praise ye, praise ye, God the Lord.

3 Rolling river, praise him ever,
　From the mountain's deep vein poured,
Silver fountain, clearly gushing,
　Sing the praises of the Lord,
Troubled torrent, madly rushing,
　Praise ye, praise ye, God the Lord:

　　Praise ye, etc.

4 Youth, whose morning smiles at warning,
　Age, in counsel deeply stored,
Each glad soul its free course winging,
　Praise him, Father, Friend, and Lord,
Each glad voice its free song singing,
　Praise the great and mighty Lord:

　　Praise ye, etc.

Professor Blackie published this rendering of the *Benedicite* in the London *Inquirer* in 1840. By the omission of some lines we have adapted it to the fine Flemish melody, 'De Dryvoudige Geboorte'.

161 THE SHEPHERD
(GENERAL)

Laurence Binyon

Austrian
(M.S.)

1. Down in the val - ley where sum - mer's laugh - ing beam
2. Ah, how they strug - gle, and pant, the sil - ly sheep,
3. Eve - ning is o - ver the land, with peace and light,

hum

Un - der the wil - low - tree lights a - long the stream,
Fear - ing the hands that dip, fear - ing wa - ter deep.
Now sits the shep - herd a - lone in eve - ning bright,

Shep - herds come driv - ing their flocks and seek the pool,
Ten - der - ly lift - ed up, glad - ly, one by one,
Now has he joy with - in, where he pi - peth low,

Plung - ing their sheep in the sun - ny wa - ter cool.
White in the green of the mea - dow, lo, they run.
See - ing his flock ga - thered round him white as snow.

The words written for the Austrian dialect folk-carol *Hirtenlied*, 'Schteff'l, du Schlafhaub'n geh' heb'
dich aus dai'm Nest', printed by F. Tschischka and J. M. Schottky in *Oesterreichische Volkslieder
mit ihren Singweisen*, Buda-Pesth, 1844.

162 BELL CAROL

(GENERAL)
JE SAIS, VIERGE MARIE
(CHRISTMAS)

Steuart Wilson

French
(M.S.)

In moderate time

SOPRANO
ALTO

1. In ev-'ry town and vil - lage The bells do
2. Then pull your ropes with vi - gour, And watch your
3. And we who hear the bells ring With all their

TENOR
BASS

ring,
ways
might,

ring, do ring, O'er woods and grass and till - age, Hey ding a ding,
ways, your ways To thread with strict - est ri - gour The noi - sy maze;
might, their might, As they do say the an - gels sing Both day and night,

ring,
ways
might,

Ring - ing for joy to start the week a - gain, And
Keep in your heart the fire of youth a - light, That
Praise we the men who built our bel - fries high That

call all Christ - ian men To pray and praise and sing.
he who rings a - right May ring in hap - py days.
mu - sic from the sky Might sound for our de - light.

330

Je sais, vierge Marie,
　　Ce que je dois
Pour fêter le Messie
　　Qu'ici je vois;
C'est mon Sauveur, dont Dieu seul est le père
　　Et vous, Vierge, la mère
　　Dont il a fait le choix.

2 Je vois en vous, Princesse,
　　Tant de bonté,
D'amour et de tendresse,
　　De charité
Que librement, aujourd'hui je demande,
　　Une grâce bien grande
　　Avec humilité.

3 Vierge sainte et parfaite
　　Ah, dites-nous,
Quel fut le doux prophète
　　Qui vint à vous,
Pour annoncer cet aimable mystère
　　Que vous seriez la mère
　　De cet enfant si doux?

4 C'était en Galilée,
　　A Nazareth,
La ville où je suis née,
　　Comme l'on sait
Dieu m'envoya le message authentique
　　D'un esprit angélique
　　Qu'on nomme Gabriel.

5 Il dit: 'Vierge Marie,
　　Croyez ma voix!
Dieu qui vous a choisie
　　Vers vous m'envoie.
Car le Seigneur connaît votre mérite;
　　En votre âme il habite
　　Et vous juge et vous voit'.

6 Donc à l'ange avec joie
　　Je répondis:
Mon Dieu qui vous envoie
　　Du paradis,
Sait que je suis sa très humble servante,
　　Toujours obéissante
　　Et que pour lui je vis.

163 THE THREE TRAITORS
(GENERAL)

Walter de la Mare

English traditional
(M.S.)

In moderate time

1. It was— a-bout the deep— of night, And
2. Be-yond— the sea, be-yond— the sea, Lie

still— was earth and sky,_____ When 'neath— the moon-light
king-doms for them all:_____ I wot— their steeds trod

dazz-ling bright, Three ghosts— came rid-ing by.____
wea-ri-ly— The jour-ney was not small.____

ALTERNATIVE VERSION (may be used for verses 3, 6, 9, & 11, or for any other selection of verses
if desired)

(Melody in Tenor)

3. By rock and des-ert, sand and stream, They foot-sore late— did go:— Now

332

like— a sweet and bless-ed dream Their path—was deep—with snow.—

4 Shining like hoar-frost, rode they on,
 Three ghosts in earth's array:
 It was about the hour when wan
 Night turns at hint of day.

5 O, but their hearts with woe distraught
 Hailed not the wane of night,
 Only for Jesu still they sought
 To wash them clean and white.

6 For bloody was each hand, and dark
 With death each orbless eye;—
 It was three Traitors mute and stark
 Came riding silent by.

7 Silver their raiment and their spurs,
 And silver-shod their feet,
 And silver-pale each face that stares
 Into the moonlight sweet.

8 And he upon the left that rode
 Was Pilate, Prince of Rome,
 Whose journey once lay far abroad,
 And now was nearing home.

9 And he upon the right that rode
 Herod of Salem sate,
 Whose mantle dipped in children's blood
 Shone clear as heaven's gate.

10 And he these twain betwixt that rode
 Was clad as white as wool,
 Dyed in the mercy of his God
 White was he crown to sole.

11 Throned mid a myriad saints in bliss
 Rise shall the Babe of heaven
 To shine on these three ghosts, I wis,
 Smit through with sorrows seven.

12 Babe of the blessèd Trinity
 Shall smile their steeds to see:
 Herod and Pilate riding by,
 And Judas one of three.

The tune from Gilbert, 1823, 'The Three Knights'.

164 CAROL OF BEAUTY
(GENERAL : PRAISE)
QUELLE EST CETTE ODEUR AGREABLE?
(CHRISTMAS)

Steuart Wilson

French
(M.S.)

1. Praise we the Lord, who made all beau - - ty
2. Praise him who makes our life a plea - - sure,

For all our sen - ses to en - joy; Give we our
Send - ing us things which glad our___ eyes; Thank him who

hum - ble thanks and du - ty That sim - ple plea - sures
gives us wel - come lei - sure, That in our heart sweet

nev - er cloy;___ Praise we the Lord who made all
thoughts may rise;___ Praise him who makes our life a

334

beau - ty For all our sen - ses to en - - joy.
plea - - sure, Send - ing us things which glad our eyes.

3 Praise him who loves to see young lovers,
   Fresh hearts that swell with youthful pride;
Thank him who sends the sun above us,
   As bridegroom fit to meet his bride;
Praise him who loves to see young lovers,
   Fresh hearts that swell with youthful pride.

4 Praise him who by a simple flower
   Lifts up our hearts to things above;
Thank him who gives to each one power
   To find a friend to know and love;
Praise him who by a simple flower
   Lifts up our hearts to things above.

5 Praise we the Lord who made all beauty
   For all our senses to enjoy;
Give we our humble thanks and duty
   That simple pleasures never cloy;
Praise we the Lord who made all beauty
   For all our senses to enjoy.

QUELLE est cette odeur agréable
   Bergers, qui ravit tous nos sens?
S'exhale-t-il rien de semblable
   Au milieu des fleurs du printemps?
Quelle est cette odeur agréable
   Bergers, qui ravit tous nos sens?

2 Mais quelle éclatante lumière
   Dans la nuit vient frapper nos yeux!
L'astre du jour, dans sa carrière,
   Fût-il jamais si radieux?
Mais quelle éclatante lumière
   Dans la nuit vient frapper nos yeux?

3 Ne craignez rien, peuple fidèle,
   Ecoutez l'ange du Seigneur;
Il vous annonce une nouvelle
   Qui va vous combler de bonheur,
Ne craignez rien, peuple fidèle,
   Ecoutez l'ange du Seigneur.

4 A Bethléem, dans une crèche,
   Il vient de vous naître un Sauveur;
Allons, que rien ne vous empêche
   D'adorer votre Rédempteur.
A Bethléem, dans une crèche,
   Il vient de vous naître un Sauveur.

5 Dieu tout-puissant, gloire éternelle
   Vous soit rendue jusqu'aux cieux;
Que la paix soit universelle,
   Que la grâce abonde en tous lieux.
Dieu tout-puissant, gloire éternelle
   Vous soit rendue jusqu'aux cieux.

Words written for the French carol, 'Quelle est cette odeur agréable'. The tune found its way to England so long ago as to appear in Gay's *Beggar's Opera*, 1728. Paul Arma, in *Noël, chantons noël*, gives two different versions: 'Bergers, écoutez la musique', and 'Viens vite, laisse ta houlette'.

165 GOLDEN MORNINGS
(GENERAL)

A.F.D.

English traditional
(M.S.)

1. They saw the light shine out a-far On Christ-mas in the morn - ing; And straight they knew it was the star That came to give them warn - ing: Then did they fall on bend - ed knee, The light their heads a-dorn - ing, And praised the

2. For three short years he went a-broad And set men's hearts a--burn - ing; That mis - sion turned the world to God And brought the night to morn - ing: He bore for man re--pulse and pain, In - gra - ti - tude, and scorn - ing; He suf - fered,

Lord, who let them see His glo - ry in the morn - ing.
died, he rose a - gain At Eas - ter in the morn - ing.

3 O every thought be of his grace,
   On each day in the morning;
And for his kingdom's loveliness
   Our souls be ever yearning:
So may we live, to heaven our hearts
   In hope for ever turning;
Then may we die, as each departs,
   In joy at our new morning.

PART 2

Paean

LIFT up your heads, rejoice and dance,
   Forget the days of mourning!
The waves of light advance, advance,
   The fire of love is burning.
Farewell to hate and stupid fears,
   To ignorance and sorrow!
He who was with us through the years
   Shall bring us to the morrow!

There are two tunes (this, from Fyfe's *Carols*, 1860, and No. 146) to which the name of 'Golden Carol' is found attached, with a pair of indifferent verses, in some publications of about ninety years ago. The name 'Golden Carol' was loosely used and was sometimes applied to 'The First Nowell'; but the real text of the Golden Carol is in a different metre, fifteenth century in its earlier form, and its tune is lost (see No. 173). The two tunes, which we are calling 'Golden Mornings' (No. 165) and 'Golden' (No. 146) are, however, fine and distinct traditional tunes; and the verses attached to them seem to contain phrases of an original which may have been sung to them. These phrases have therefore been retained in this new text, which may be sung equally well to No. 146.

Part 2 has been supplied for occasions when one concluding verse is needed for a carol recital or service (cf. No. 16); it can also be treated as a fourth verse to this carol.

166 CAROL OF SERVICE

(GENERAL)

PROMPTEMENT LEVEZ-VOUS

(CHRISTMAS)

Steuart Wilson

French
(M.S.)

Moderately quick

1. Up, my neigh-bour, come a - way, See the work for us to-
2. Up, my neigh-bour, see the plough For our hands lies wait - ing

-day, The hands to help, the mouths to feed, The sights to
now; Grasp well the stilt, yoke up the team, Stride out to

see, the books to read: *Up and get us gone, to help the world a-*
meet the morn - ing beam:

-long,   Up   and   get   us   gone,   my   neigh - bour.

338

3 Up, my neighbour, see the land
  Ready for the sower's hand;
  The plough has made an even tilth,
  The furrows wait the golden spilth:

  Up and get etc.

4 Up, my neighbour, now the corn
  Ripens at the harvest morn;
  Then let it to our sickle yield,
  And pile with sheaves the golden field:

  Up and get etc.

5 Up, my neighbour, let us pray,
  Thank our Maker every day,
  Who gave us work our strength to test
  And made us proud to do our best:

  Up and get etc.

PROMPTEMENT levez-vous, mon voisin,
Le Sauveur de la terre
Est enfin parmi nous, mon voisin,
Envoyé par son père, mon voisin.

Allez, mon voisin, à la crèche, mon voisin,
Courez, mon voisin, à la crèche.

2 Veillant sur mon troupeau, mon voisin,
  Autour de ce village
  J'entends un air nouveau, mon voisin,
  Et du plus beau langage, mon voisin.

  Allez, etc.

3 Rempli d'étonnement, mon voisin,
  Je laisse ma houlette
  Pour voir ce Dieu naissant, mon voisin,
  Accomplir le prophète, mon voisin.

  Allez, etc.

4 Je ne suis pas trompeur, mon voisin,
  Les choses sont certaines;
  Notre divin Sauveur, mon voisin,
  Finit toutes nos peines, mon voisin.

  Allez, etc.

5 Choisissez le meilleur, mon voisin,
  De votre bergerie,
  Donnez-le de bon coeur, mon voisin,
  A Joseph, à Marie, mon voisin.

  Allez, etc.

6 L'enfer est confondu, mon voisin,
  Le ciel a la victoire;
  Le Messie attendu, mon voisin,
  Chantons, chantons sa gloire, mon voisin.

  Allez, etc.

'Promptement levez-vous, mon voisin', upon which the English words are based, is an example of a carol made up for a familiar folk-tune, in this case an old ritournelle, 'C'est de nos moutons l'allure, mon cousin'. The carol is sung in many parts of France, and is printed by Grimault and by Legeay.

167 CAROL OF THE KINGDOM
(GENERAL)

Steuart Wilson

Manx
(M.S.)

ba - by__
car-pen-ter,

SOPRANO
ALTO

1. When Je - sus was a ba - by And born of mor - tal men, The
2. When Je - sus was a car-pen-ter, He held the saw and adze, And

TENOR
BASS

first who asked to see__ him Came straight from their sheep-pen: So
learned a trade to fol - low Like oth - er sim - ple lads: So

let_ each one re - mem - ber, When he his off - 'ring brings, __ That
let_ us not be sha - med Of hon - est work and sweat, __ Re-

Je - sus loved the shep - herds As well as the three kings.
-mem - b'ring that a bet - ter brow Than ours was of - ten wet.

3 When Jesus was a-dying
　Upon the cruel tree,
Two thieves upon each hand of him
　He had for company:
So look not upon any man
　With vain or scornful eyes,
For one poor thief was called by him
　To dwell in paradise.

4 Now Jesus has gone up on high,
　And truth and justice reign.
Let tenderness and kindliness
　Dwell in the hearts of men:
So, when we have to leave this earth,
　If only we can know
We leave it better than we found,
　We shall be glad to go.

The tune is a traditional Manx carol-tune 'Ny Drogh Vraane',
noted by the late Dr. John Clague, apparently from T. Cowell, Marown.

PART IV

TRADITIONAL CAROLS

(together with some by old writers)

SET TO TUNES BY MODERN COMPOSERS

168 BEN JONSON'S CAROL
(CHRISTMAS EVE: CHRISTMAS)

Ben Jonson

Rutland Boughton

SOPRANO
ALTO

1. I sing the birth was born_to-night, The au-thor both of
2. The Son of God, th'e-ter-nal King, That did_us all sal-

TENOR
BASS

life_and light; The an-gels so__ did sound__ it, And,
-va-tion bring, And freed our soul__from dan - - ger, He

like the_ra-vished shep-herds said, Who_ saw the light,_ and_
whom the_whole world could_ not take, The_Word, which heav'n and_

were_ a-fraid, Yet searched, and true_ they found it.
earth_ did_make, Was now_ laid in__ a man - - ger.

3 The Father's wisdom willed it so,
   The Son's obedience knew no No;
   Both wills were in one stature,
   And, as that wisdom had decreed,
   The Word was now made flesh indeed,
   And took on him our nature.

4 What comfort by him we do win,
   Who made himself the price of sin,
   To make us heirs of glory!
   To see this babe, all innocence,
   A martyr born in our defence,
   Can man forget the story?

169 TYRLEY, TYRLOW
(CHRISTMAS)

c. 1450

Peter Warlock

343

saw— a light: *Tyr - ley, tyr - - low, tyr - ley, tyr - -

-low, tyr - ley, tyr - low!

Ob., cl. & fag.

Strings sustain

Female voices in unison

2. Of an - gels there came a

Strings

*Pronunciation nearer to *tyrol-y* than *turl-y*.

345

346

-ley, tyr - low, tyr - ley, tyr - low, tyr - ley, tyr - low!___

Soprano solo *(or soprano semi- chorus)*

4. Now

pray we to that me - ke child, And to his mo - ther that

is so___ mild, The which___ was nev - er de - filed:

347

349

From the *Commonplace Book* of Richard Hill (cf. No. 36), c. 1500, and the Bodleian MS. (Engl. Poet. e. I), 1460-90, the latter printed by Wright, *Songs and Carols* (Percy Society), 1847, and Greene, No. 79.

170 NEW PRINCE, NEW POMP
(CHRISTMAS)

Robert Southwell   John Ireland

No - well, — No - well, No - well, — sing we with mirth!

Christ is come well, with us — to dwell, By — his — most

no - ble birth. —

1. Be - hold — a sim - ple ten - der
2. The inns — are full; no man — will

babe, In — freez - ing win - ter night, In — home - ly
yield This lit - tle pil - grim bed; But — forced — he

man - ger trem - bling lies: A - las! a pit - eous sight.
is with sim - ple beasts In crib to shroud his head.

3 Despise him not for lying there;
　　First what he is inquire:
　An orient pearl is often found
　　In depth of dirty mire.

4 Weigh not his crib, his wooden dish,
　　Nor beasts that by him feed;
　Weigh not his mother's poor attire,
　　Nor Joseph's simple weed.

5 This stable is a prince's court,
　　This crib his chair of state,
　The beasts are parcel of his pomp,
　　The wooden dish his plate;

6 The persons in that poor attire
　　His royal liveries wear;
　The Prince himself is come from heaven.
　　This pomp is prizèd there.

7 With joy approach, O Christian wight,
　　Do homage to thy King;
　And highly praise this humble pomp,
　　Which he from heaven doth bring.

1 and 2. We have altered 'silly' to its modern equivalent 'simple'.　5. *Parcel* in the old sense of 'part' (from 'particella', 'parcelle').
　　The prelude 'Nowell', &c., is an old prelude, but not by Southwell.
　　Robert Southwell was the good Jesuit, executed for treason under Elizabeth.

171 SHAKESPEARE'S CAROL
(CHRISTMAS, Secular)

FIRST TUNE

Dr. Arne
(arr. M.S.)

1. Blow, blow,_ thou_ win - ter
   freeze, thou_ bit - ter

wind,_ Thou art_ not_ so un - kind,_ Thou art not so un-
sky,_ That dost_ not_ bite so nigh_ As ben - e - fits for-

-kind As man's in - gra - ti - tude; Thy tooth is not so
-got, As ben - e - fits_ for-got: Though thou the wa - ters

171 SHAKESPEARE'S CAROL
(CHRISTMAS, Secular)

SECOND TUNE

R.J.S. Stevens

356

cresc.

-to the green hol-ly: Most friend-ship is feign - ing, most

cresc.

lov-ing mere fol-ly: Then, heigh - ho, the hol-ly, the hol-ly! This

life ___ is most jol - ly, most jol - ly, this life ___ is most

jol - ly, most jol - ly, this life ___ is most jol - ly! ___

Fine

Tempo I mo

2. Freeze, freeze, thou bit - ter ___ sky, ___ That dost not

357

From *As You Like It*, Act II. Dr. Arne does not include the chorus, as Stevens does.

172 MAKE WE MERRY
(CHRISTMAS, Secular)

c. 1500

Martin Shaw

1. Make we mer-ry, both more and less, For now is the time of Chris-te-mas, of Chris-te-mas, of Chris-te-mas.

2. Let no man come in-to this hall, Nor groom, nor page, nor yet mar-shall, But that some sport he bring with-al.

3. If that he say he can-not sing, Some o-ther sport then let him bring, That it may please at this feast-ing.

4. If he say he naught can do, Then, for my love, ask him no mo' But to the stocks — then let him

go.
5. Make we mer-ry, both more and less, For
now is the time of Chris-te-mas, of Christ-mas, of Christ-mas, of
Christ - - - - - - - mas.

Copyright, 1926, by Martin Shaw

1. more and less—in the old sense, 'great and small'. 4. mo'—more. stocks—The Lord of Misrule at Christmas often had stocks, pillory, and gibbet.
From the *Commonplace Book* of Richard Hill (cf. No. 36), and Balliol MS. 354. See Greene, No. 11.

173 THE GOLDEN CAROL
(CHRISTMAS: EPIPHANY)

15th century

R. Vaughan Williams

Allegro vivace

VOICES IN UNISON

1. __ Now is Chris-te-mas y-come, Fa-ther and Son_ to-
3. Three king-es came fro Ga-li-lee To Beth-le-hem, that
5. 'From whence come ye, you king-es three?' 'Out of the East, as
7. __ When they came in-to the place, Where Je-sus with_ his
8. __ Kneel we now__ here a-down; Pray we in good de-

ACCPT.

Marcato

-ge-ther in one, Ho-ly Ghost, as ye __ be one, __ In
fair __ ci-ty, For_ to of-fer and_ to see, __ By
ye __ may see, To __ seek him that ev-er shall be, __ By
mo-ther was, Of-fer'd they up with great_ so-lace, __ In
-vo-ti-oun, To_ that King of great_ re-nown,_ For

fere-a, God send __ us good new year-a.
night-a, It was __ a full fair sight-a.
right-a, __ Lord __ and king and knight-a.'
fere-a, __ Gold, __ in-cense, and myrrh-a.
grace-a, In heav'n __ to have a place-a.

362

2. I will you sing with all my might, Of a child— so
4. As they came forth with their offer-ing, They met with Her-od, that
6. They took their leave, both eld and ying, Of Her-od,— that

fair in sight, A maid-en bare on Christ-mas night,— So
mood-y king, He ask-ed them of their com-ing,— That
mood-y king, And forth they went with their offer-ing— By

still-a,— As— it was his will-a.
tide-a, And thus— to them he said-a:
light-a, By the star— that shone so bright-a.

Copyright, 1928, by R. Vaughan Williams

6. eld and ying—old and young. 7. Where—orig. MS., 'There' with this meaning.
    This, which has most right to the name, 'Golden Carol', was printed by T. Wright from the Bodleian MS. Eng. Poet. e. I (c. 1460-90) in his *Songs and Carols* (Percy Society), 1847; also by Sandys in his *Christmas Tide*, 1852; A. H. Bullen (*Carols and Poems*, 1885) prints another version from *Notes and Queries*. Miss E. Rickert (*Ancient English Christmas Carols*, 1910) gives two versions, one in sixteen verses and without the tag. We have used that by Mr. F. Sidgwick in *Ancient Carols*, 1908. Greene, No. 125, gives a version from B. M. Harley 541. No tune has survived. Cf. Nos. 146 and 165.

174 WELCOME YULE
(CHRISTMAS, ST. STEPHEN, ETC.: CANDLEMAS)

15th century

Sydney H. Nicholson

3. in fere—together   lief—beloved

Sloane MS. 2593 (cf. No. 36), of the beginning of the fifteenth century or *temp.* Henry VI. Another version in the Bodleian Douce MS. 302, the collection of John Audlay, the blind chaplain, *c.* 1430, printed in Sandys' *Christmastide*, 1852. See Preface. Greene, No. 7.

175 THE VIRGIN'S CRADLE HYMN
(NATIVITY)

Pr. S. T. Coleridge

Edmund Rubbra

ma - - ter plo - - rat In - ter fil - a can - tans o - rat,
mo - - ther mourn - eth, Sing - ing as her wheel she turn - eth:

ma - - ter plo - - rat In - ter fil - a can - tans o - rat,
mo - - ther mourn - eth, Sing - ing as her wheel she turn - eth:

ma - ter plo - - rat In - ter fil - a can - tans o - rat,
mo - - ther mourn - eth, Sing - ing as her wheel she turn - eth:

ma - ter plo - - rat In - ter fil - a can - tans o - rat,
mo - ther mourn - eth, Sing - ing as her wheel she turn - eth:

Blan - de, ven - i, som - nu - le.
Come, soft slum - ber, balm - i - ly!

Blan - de, ven - i, som - nu - le.
Come, soft slum - ber, balm - i - ly!

Blan - de, ven - i, som - nu - le.
Come, - soft - slum - ber, balm - i - ly!

Blan - de, ven - i, som - nu - le.
Come, soft - slum - ber, balm - i - ly!

Coleridge copied the Latin words from a print in a German village, and paraphrased them as
printed, under the title 'The Virgin's Cradle Hymn'. These verses are therefore akin to such
Cradle Hymns as the Chester Nuns' Song (No. 67), 'Lullay, my liking' (No. 182), and the Lute Book
Lullaby (No. 30).

176 HERRICK'S ODE
(NATIVITY)

Robert Herrick

Armstrong Gibbs

1. In num-bers, and but these few, I sing thy birth, O
2. In-stead of neat en-clo-sures Of in-ter-wo-ven

Je-su, Thou pret-ty ba-by, born here, With su-pera-bun-dant
o-siers; In-stead of fra-grant po-sies Of daf-fo-dils and

scorn here, Who for thy prince-ly port here, Hadst
ro-ses, Thy cra-dle, king-ly stran-ger, As

for thy place Of birth, a base Out-sta-ble for thy court here.
gos-pel tells, Was no-thing else But here a home-ly man-ger.

3 But we with silks, not crewels,
  With sundry precious jewels,
  And lily-work will dress thee;
  And, as we dispossess thee
  Of clouts, we'll make a chamber,
    Sweet babe, for thee,
    Of ivory,
  And plastered round with amber.

4 The Jews, they did disdain thee,
  But we will entertain thee
  With glories to await here
  Upon thy princely state here,
  And, more for love than pity,
    From year to year
    We'll make here
  A free-born of our city.

177 OUT OF YOUR SLEEP
(NATIVITY)

15th century

Martin Shaw

Rather slowly

SOPRANO
ALTO

1. Out of your sleep a-rise and wake, For God man-
2. And through a maid-e fair and wise Now man is
4. That ev-er was thrall, now is he free; That ev-er was
6. Now, bless-ed Broth-er, grant us grace, At doom-es

TENOR
BASS

-kind now hath y-take All of a maid with-out a-ny
made of full great price; Now an-gels kne-len to man's ser-
small, now great is she; Now shall God deem both thee and
day to see thy face, And in thy court to have a

the bell.
be - fell.
do well.
no - well.

make; Of all wo-men she bear-eth the bell, the bell.
-vice, And at this time all this be-fell, be-fell.
me Un-to his bliss, if we do well, do well.
place, That we may there sing thee no-well, no-well.

Of all wo-men she bear-eth the bell.
And at this time all this be-fell.
Un-to his bliss, if we do well.
That we may there sing thee no-well.

For fa-burden to vv. 3 and 5 see overleaf.

3 Now man is brighter than the sun;
Now man in heaven on high shall won;
Blessèd be God this game is begun
And his mother empress of hell.

5 Now man he may to heaven wend;
Now heaven and earth to him they bend;
He that was foe now is our friend.
This is no nay that I you tell.

5

Bless - ed be God this game is be - gun
He that was foe now is our_ friend.

Bless - ed be God, And his
This is no nay, This is

God this game is be - gun And his
foe now is_ our friend. This is

-ed be God, be God,
is no nay, no nay,

And his mo - - ther em - press of hell.
This is no nay that I you tell.

mo - - ther em - - press_ of hell.
no nay that I_ you tell.

mo - ther em - press_ of hell.
no nay that I_ you tell.

And his mo - ther em - press of hell.
This is no nay that I you tell.

3. won—dwell. 4. deem—judge. 5. no nay—not to be denied.
This fine carol is from the Selden MS. at Oxford, *c.* 1450, printed in Greene, No. 30, and in *Mediaeval Carols*, No. 25, with the original words. This setting is founded on a Danish chime.

178 IN EXCELSIS GLORIA
(NATIVITY)

FIRST TUNE

1456

A. H. Brown

OPTIONAL INTRODUCTION

mf

S.
A.

1. When Christ was born of__ Ma - ry__ free, In
3. This King is come to__ save his__ kind, ____

T.
B.

Beth - lem in that fair ci - ty, An - gels sung e'er with
In the script - ure as we__ find; There - fore this song have

mirth and glee,
we in mind: *In ex - cel - sis__ glo - ri - a,*

p

CHORUS

In ex-cel-sis glo-ri - a, In ex-cel-sis glo-ri - a,

In ex-cel-sis_ glo-ri - a, In ex_-cel-sis glo-ri - a.

VERSES 2 & 4

2. Herd-men be - held these_ an - gels_ bright— To
4. Then,_ dear Lord, for_ thy great_ grace, Grant

them ap-pear - ed with great_ light, And said, 'God's Son is
us in bliss to see thy_ face, Where we may sing to

born   this   night':
thy   so - lace:
In   ex - cel - sis___ glo - ri - a,

CHORUS

In   ex-cel - sis   glo - ri - a,   In   ex-cel - sis   glo - ri - a,

In   ex - cel - sis___ glo - ri - a,   In___ ex - cel - sis   glo - ri - a.

D.S.

See footnote to second tune.

178 IN EXCELSIS GLORIA
(NATIVITY)

SECOND TUNE

1456

Martin Shaw

SOLO VOICE

Christ - o pa - re - mus can - ti - ca, In ex - cel - sis glo - ri - a.

(Omit in v. 4)

SOPRANO
ALTO

1. When Christ was born of Ma - ry free, In Beth - lem in that
2. Herd - men be - held these an - gels bright—To them ap - pear - ed

TENOR
BASS

fair ci - ty, An - gels sung e'er with mirth and glee,
with great light, And said, 'God's Son is born this night':

In ex - cel - sis glo - - ri - a.

In ex - cel - sis glo - - ri - a.

3 This King is come to save his kind,
In the scripture as we find;
Therefore this song have we in mind:

   In excelsis gloria.

4 Then, dear Lord, for thy great grace,
Grant us in bliss to see thy face,
Where we may sing to thy solace:

   In excelsis gloria.

Harleian MS. 5396 (c. 1450). Printed Wright, &c., and Chambers and Sidgwick, and Greene, No. 80.
Original tune lost; A. H. Brown's tune appeared in Bramley & Stainer, 1871. Beyond the moderniz-
ing of the spelling, the following lines of the original only are altered: v. I. 'Angellis songen with
mirth and glee', v. 3. 'This king is comen to save kinde', v. 4. 'Then Lord, for thy gret grace'.

179 THE QUEST

MARIAS WALLFAHRT
(THE PASSION)

Traditional, tr. H. T. Wade-Gery

J. Brahms

Con moto

SOPRANO
1. Saint Ma - ry goes a - seek - ing Through Jew - ry up and
2. O look, for she has found him; By He - rod's house stood

ALTO
1. Saint Ma - ry goes a - seek - ing Through Jew - ry up and
2. O — look, for she has found — him; By He - rod's house stood

TENOR
1. Saint Ma - ry goes a - seek - ing Through Jew - ry up — and
2. O — look, for she has found — him; By He - rod's house stood

BASS
1. Saint Ma - ry goes a - seek - ing Through Jew - ry up and
2. O look, for she has found him; By He - rod's house stood

down, Through Jew - ry up and down, Un - til God the Lord she found.
he, By He - rod's house stood he, What sor - row for her to see!

down, Through Jew - ry up and down, Un - til God the Lord she found.
he, By He - rod's house stood he, What sor - row for her to see!

down, Through Jew - ry up and down, Un - til God the Lord she found.
he, By He - rod's house stood he, What sor - row for her to see!

down, Through Jew - ry up and down, Un - til God the Lord she found.
he, By He - rod's house stood he, What sor - row for her to see!

-lem, To where he will suf-fer shame.
thorn, The cross__ on__shoul-der borne!
5. O young and old, look

-lem, To where he will suf-fer shame.
thorn, The cross__ on shoul-der borne!
5. O young and old, look

-lem, To where he will suf-fer shame.
thorn, The cross__ on shoul-der borne!
5. O young and old, look

-lem, To where he will suf-fer shame.
thorn, The cross__ on shoul-der borne!
5. O young and old, look

to it; Ye nev-er this for-get,___

to it; Ye nev-er this for-get,___

to it; Ye nev-er this for-get,___

to it; Ye nev-er this for-get,___

That his wounds set wide high hea - ven's gate! _____

That his wounds set wide high hea - ven's gate! _____

That his wounds set wide high hea - ven's gate! _____

That his wounds set wide high hea - ven's gate! _____

MARIA ging aus wandern
So fern ins fremde Land
Bis sie Gott den Herren fand.

2 Sie hat ihn schon gefunden
Wohl vor des Herodes Haus,
Er sah so betrüblich aus.

3 Das Kreuz, das musst' er tragen
Nach Jerusalem vor die Stadt
Wo er gemartert ward.

4 Was trug er auf seinem Haupte?
Ein' scharfe Dornenkron,
Das Kreuz, das trug er schon.

5 Daran soll man bedenken,
Ein jeder, jung or alt,
Dass das Himmelreich leidet Gewalt.

'Marias Wallfahrt' ('Maria ging aus wandern') is given here as it was set by Brahms in his *Marien-lieder*, with a new translation of the words. The second line in each verse is repeated. Cf. No. 93.

180 ADAM LAY YBOUNDEN
(GENERAL, Medieval)

c. 15th century

Peter Warlock

1. A - dam lay y - boun - den, Boun - den in a bond; Four thou - sand win - ter Thought he not too long. 2. And all was for an ap - ple, An ap - ple that he took, As clerk - es find - en writ - ten In their book. 3. Ne

From the Sloane MS. 2593 (fifteenth century). Printed Wright, &c., and Chambers and Sidgwick.

181 BALULALOW
(GENERAL)

Wedderburn, 1567

Peter Warlock

382

383

1. spreit—spirit. sall—shall. 2. sangis—songs. gloir—glory.
From 'Ane Sang of the birth of Christ' ('I come from heaven to tell'), a piece of fifteen stanzas, from *Ane Compendious Buik of Godly and Spirituall Sangis*, 1567, by the brothers James, John, and Robert Wedderburn. The whole poem is a translation of the Christmas Eve Carol which Luther wrote for his son Hans, 'Vom Himmel hoch', first published in *Geistliche Lieder*, 1535. Luther's tune is in *Songs of Praise*, No. 80.

182 LULLAY MY LIKING
(GENERAL, Medieval)

15th century

Gustav Holst

SOPRANO ALTO

TENOR BASS

REFRAIN
Allegretto

Lul - lay my lik - ing, my dear son, my sweet - ing;

Lul - lay my dear heart, mine own dear dar - ling!

SOLO

1. I saw a fair maid - en Sit - ten and sing: She

lul - led a lit - tle child, A swee - te lord - ing:

REFRAIN

Lul - lay my lik - ing, my dear son, my sweet - ing;

Lul - lay my dear heart, mine own dear dar - ling!

2. That e - ter - nal Lord is he That made al - le thing; Of
al - le lord - es he is Lord, Of al - le king - es King:

REFRAIN

Lul - lay my lik - ing, my dear son, my sweet - ing;

Lul - lay my dear heart, mine own dear dar - ling!

3. There was mic - kle mel - o - dy At that child - es birth: Al - though
they were in hea-ven's bliss They ma - de mic - kle mirth:

387

REFRAIN

Lul - lay my lik - ing, my dear son, my sweet - ing;

Lul - lay my dear heart, mine own dear dar - ling!

CHORUS

4. An - gels bright they sang that night And said - en to that child 'Bless-ed be

thou, and so be she That is both meek and mild':

REFRAIN

Lul - lay my lik - ing, my dear son, my sweet - ing;

Lul - lay my dear heart, mine own dear dar - ling!

SOLO

5. Pray we now to that child, And to his mo - ther dear, God
grant them all his bless - ing That now mak - en cheer:

REFRAIN

Lul - lay my lik - ing, my dear son, my sweet - ing;

Lul - lay my dear heart, mine own dear dar - ling!

By permission from Curwen Edition No. 80589.

2. eternal—orig. 'eche', with the same meaning. 3. mickle—much.
Words from the Sloane MS. (see Nos. 116, 174, 180, 183).
Greene (No. 143) calls this 'the masterpiece of the lullaby carols' and is
inclined to attribute it to the same unknown author as the carol that follows.

183 I SING OF A MAIDEN
(GENERAL, Medieval)

15th century   Martin Shaw

SOLO VOICE
Rather slowly

1. I sing of a maid - en That is makè - less;
King of all kings To her son she ches.

CHORUS (VERSES 2, 3, & 4)
Slow

2. He came all so still Where his mo - ther was, As
3. He came all so still To his mo - ther's bowr, As
4. He came all so still Where his mo - ther lay, As

2,3,4. He came all so still, so still, As

2. He came all so still Where his mo - ther was, As
3. He came all so still To his mo - ther's bowr, As
4. He came all so still Where his mo - ther lay, As

2,3,4. He came all so still, so still, As

dew in A - pril That fall - eth on the grass.
dew in A - pril That fall - eth on the flower.
dew in A - pril That fall - eth on the spray.

390

(VERSE 5)
pp Slow

5. Mo - ther   and maid - en   Was   nev - er none but   she;

Well   may such a   la - dy   God - es mo - ther   be.

Copyright, 1928, by Martin Shaw

1. makèless—matchless.   ches (pronounce to rhyme with 'less')—chose.   2, 4. Where —*orig*. MS. 'There.' with this meaning.   all so—*orig*. 'also', as.

This famous little classic is also in the Sloane MS. Of its 'ineffable grace' Prof. Saintsbury says: 'In no previous verse had this Aeolian music—this "harp of Ariel"—that distinguishes English at its very best in this direction . . . been given to the world' (*Short History of English Literature*, 1913, p. 202). If ever there was a tune, it has been lost.

184 ALL BELLS IN PARADISE
(GENERAL)

Traditional

Martin Shaw

SOLO
1. O - ver yon - der's a park, which is new - ly be - gun:
2. And in that park there stands a hall:

A.T.B. hum

SOLO
(1.) Which is
(2.) Which is

CHORUS (all sing words)

All bells in pa - ra - dise I heard them a - ring, (A.T.B. hum)

sil - ver on the out - side and gold_ with - in:
cov - ered all_ o - ver with pur - ple and pall;

CHORUS

And I

love___ sweet Je - sus a - bove___ all thing.

3 And in that hall there stands a bed:
   Which is hung all round with silk curtains so red:

4 And in that bed there lies a knight:
   Whose wounds they do bleed by day and by night:

5 At that bedside there lies a stone:
   Which our blest Virgin Mary knelt upon:

6 At that bed's foot there lies a hound:
   Which is licking the blood as it daily runs down:

7 At that bed's head there grows a thorn:
   Which was never so blossomed since Christ was born:

See No. 61 for the version with its traditional tune. This version was recovered in the middle of the nineteenth century in North Staffordshire and contributed to *Notes and Queries* in 1862, but without its tune. The theme is still eucharistic: v. 3 describes the altar with dorsal and riddels; v. 7 the Glastonbury thorn. See Greene, No. 322.

185 WITHER'S ROCKING HYMN
(GENERAL)

George Wither

R. Vaughan Williams

1. Sweet ba- by, sleep! What ails my dear?
2. Whilst thus thy lul - la- by I sing,

What ails my dar - ling thus to cry? Be still, my
For thee great bless - ings ripe - ning be; Thine el - dest

child, and lend thine ear To hear me sing thy
bro - ther is a King, And hath a king - dom

lul - la - by.　My pret-ty lamb, for - bear___ to weep;
bought_ for thee.　Sweet ba - by, then, for - bear___ to weep;

s. *pp* Chorus unaccompanied

A.

Sweet _____ ba - - - by,

T.

B.

pp

Be still, my dear;　sweet ba - by, sleep.
Be still, my babe;　sweet ba - by, sleep.

sleep,_____　sweet ba - by, sleep.

Copyright, 1928, by R. Vaughan Williams

3 When God with us was dwelling here,
　In little babes he took delight:
Such innocents as thou, my dear,
　Are ever precious in his sight.
　　Sweet baby, then, forbear to weep;
　　Be still, my babe; sweet baby, sleep.

4 A little infant once was he,
　And strength in weakness then was laid
Upon his virgin mother's knee,
　That power to thee might be conveyed.
　　Sweet baby, then, forbear to weep;
　　Be still, my babe; sweet baby, sleep.

5 The King of kings, when he was born,
　Had not so much for outward ease;
By him such dressings were not worn,
　Nor suchlike swaddling-clothes as these.
　　Sweet baby, then, forbear to weep;
　　Be still, my babe; sweet baby, sleep.

6 The wants that he did then sustain
　Have purchased wealth, my babe, for thee;
And by his torments and his pain
　Thy rest and ease securèd be.
　　My baby, then, forbear to weep;
　　Be still, my babe; sweet baby, sleep.

George Wither's most famous lyrics were early written, 'Shall I wasting in despair' in 1615. He became a Puritan in 1623, and was raising a troop of horse in 1642. The 'Rocking Hymn' was in *Halelujah*, 1641.

O

PART V
CAROLS BY MODERN
WRITERS AND COMPOSERS

186 SNOW IN THE STREET
(CHRISTMAS)

William Morris

R. Vaughan Williams

Andante con moto ($\mathbf{\natural} \cdot = $ **about 63**)

VOICES IN
UNISON

1. From far a-way we come to you, *The*
2. For as we wan-dered far and wide,

ORGAN
(OR VOICES
IN HARMONY)

snow in the street and the wind on the door, To tell of great
What hap do you

ti - dings strange and true.
deem there should us be - tide? *Min - strels and maids stand*

forth on the floor: From far a-way we come_ to you, To tell of great ti - dings strange _____ and true._____

3 Under a bent when the night was deep,
   There lay three shepherds tending their sheep:

4 'O ye shepherds, what have ye seen,
   To slay your sorrow and heal your teen?'

5 'In an ox-stall this night we saw
   A babe and a maid without a flaw:

Part 2

6 'There was an old man there beside;
   His hair was white, and his hood was wide:

7 'And as we gazed this thing upon,
   Those twain knelt down to the little one.

8 'And a marvellous song we straight did hear,
   That slew our sorrow and healed our care.'

9 News of a fair and a marvellous thing,
   Nowell, Nowell, Nowell, we sing!

From William Morris's *The Earthly Paradise* (1868-70) in the poem, 'The Land East of the Sun and West of the Moon'. The carol begins 'Outlanders, whence came ye last', the first, second, and fourth verses being here omitted.

187 MID-WINTER
(CHRISTMAS)

Christina Rossetti

Gustav Holst

In moderate time

SOPRANO
ALTO

TENOR
BASS

1. In the bleak mid - win - ter Frost - y wind made moan,
2. Our God, heav'n can - not hold_ him Nor_ earth sus - tain:
3. E - nough for him, whom che - ru - bim Wor - ship night and day, A
4. An - gels and arch - an - gels May have ga - thered there,
5. What_ can I give_ him, Poor_ as I am?

Earth stood hard as i - ron, Wa - ter like a stone;
Heav'n and earth shall flee a - way When he comes to reign:
breast - - ful of milk, _ And a man - ger - ful of hay; E -
Che - ru - bim and se - ra - phim Thronged _ the air: But
If I were a shep - herd I would bring a lamb;

Snow had fal - len, snow on snow, Snow_ on _ snow,
In the bleak mid - win - ter A sta - ble - place suf - ficed The
-nough for him, whom an - gels Fall_ down be - fore, The
on - ly his mo - ther In her maid - en bliss
If I were a wise_ man I would do my part; Yet

In the bleak mid - win - ter, Long_ a - go.
Lord_ God Al - might - y Je - sus_ Christ.
ox and ass and ca - mel Which_ a - dore.
Wor - shipped the Be - lov - ed With_ a _ kiss.
what I can I give him— Give_ my _ heart.

This poem, with its tune from the *English Hymnal*
and *Songs of Praise*, is so much a carol that we feel bound to include it here also.

188 OUR BROTHER IS BORN
(CHRISTMAS)

Eleanor Farjeon

Harry Farjeon

1. Now ev - 'ry child that dwells on earth, Stand
2. Now ev - 'ry star that dwells in sky, Look
3. Now ev - 'ry beast that crops in field, Breathe
4. Now ev - 'ry bird that flies in air, Sing,

up, stand up and sing:＿＿ The pass - ing night has
down with shi - ning eyes:＿＿ The night has dropped in
sweet - ly and a - dore:＿＿ The night has brought the
ra - ven, lark, and dove:＿＿ The night has brood - ed

188—Our Brother is Born

giv - en birth Un - to the child - ren's King.____
pass - ing by A Star from pa - ra - dise.____
rich - est yield That e'er the har - vest bore.____
on her lair And fledged the Bird of love.____

Sing sweet as the flute, Sing clear as the horn, Sing

joy of the child - ren, stars, ____ creat - ures, birds, ____ Come Christ - mas the morn:

Lit - tle Christ Je - sus Our bro - ther is born.____

5.* Now

Moderato
all the an-gels of the Lord, Rise up on Christ-mas

+Even:_____ The pass-ing night will hear the Word That

Poco meno mosso
is the voice of heav'n.__ Sing sweet as the flute, Sing

+ Pronounce nearly as one syllable

clear as the horn, Sing joy of the an - gels, Come

Christ- mas the morn: *Lit - tle Christ Je - sus Our bro - ther is*

mp cresc. *allarg.*

Allegretto

born.

f cresc. *ff* *f*

For high voices this carol may be transposed to key E.

189 MERRY CHRISTMAS
(CHRISTMAS, Secular)

Adapted from
Sir Walter Scott

Martin Shaw

On Christ-mas Eve the bells were rung, On

Christ-mas Eve the mass was sung;⸺ The dam-sel donn'd her

kir-tle sheen, The hall was dress'd with hol-ly green;⸺

Forth to the wood did mer-ry-men go, To gath-er in the mis-tle-toe:____

(CHORUS)

Then drink to the hol-ly ber-ry, With hey down, hey down der-ry! The mis-tle-toe we'll pledge al-so, And at Christ-mas all be mer-ry, At Christ - - mas all be mer - ry. ____

-cen - - do *ff*

2. The fire, with well-dried

loco

dim - in - u - en - do *f*

logs sup - plied, Went roar - ing up the chim - ney wide; ____ Then

came the mer - ry mas - quers in, And car - ols roared with

blithe - some din._____ Eng - land is mer - ry

Eng - land, when Old Christ - mas brings his sports a - gain:_____

Then drink to the hol - ly ber - ry, *With*

The words are taken from *Marmion*, introduction to Canto VI; with a traditional refrain added.

190 WINTER'S SNOW
(CHRISTMAS)

FIRST TUNE

E. Caswall

J. Goss

SOLO (soprano or tenor, or alternately)

Moderato

VOICE

1. See a-mid the win-ter's snow, Born for us on earth be-low;
2. Lo, with-in a man-ger lies He who built the star-ry skies;

ACCPT.

See the ten-der Lamb ap-pears, Pro-mised from e-ter-nal years:
He who, throned in height sub-lime, Sits a-mid the che-ru-bim:

CHORUS

S.
A.

Hail, thou ev-er-bless-ed morn; Hail, re-demp-tion's hap-py dawn;

T.
B.

Sing through all Je - ru - sa - lem, ___ Christ is born in Beth- le - hem.

3 Say, ye holy shepherds, say
What your joyful news to-day;
Wherefore have ye left your sheep
On the lonely mountain steep?

Hail, thou ever-blessed morn; etc.

4 'As we watched at dead of night,
Lo, we saw a wondrous light;
Angels singing "Peace on earth"
Told us of the Saviour's birth':

Hail, thou ever-blessed morn; etc.

5 Sacred infant, all divine,
What a tender love was thine,
Thus to come from highest bliss
Down to such a world as this:

Hail, thou ever-blessed morn; etc.

6 Teach, O teach us, holy Child,
By thy face so meek and mild,
Teach us to resemble thee,
In thy sweet humility:

Hail, thou ever-blessed morn; etc.

The familiar tune by John Goss appeared in Bramley and Stainer's *Christmas Carols New and Old*.

190 WINTER'S SNOW
(CHRISTMAS)
SECOND TUNE

E. Caswall

R.O. Morris

1. See a-mid the win-ter's snow, Born for us on earth be-low;
2. Lo, with-in a man-ger lies He who built the star-ry skies;

See the ten-der Lamb ap-pears, Pro-mised from e-ter-nal years:
He who, throned in height sub-lime, Sits a-mid the che-ru-bim:

CHORUS

Hail, thou ev-er-bless-ed morn; Hail, re-demp-tion's hap-py dawn;

(Accpt. *ad lib.*)

Sing through all Je - ru - sa - lem, ___ Christ is born in ___ Beth- le - hem.

3 Say, ye holy shepherds, say
What your joyful news to-day;
Wherefore have ye left your sheep
On the lonely mountain steep?

Hail, thou ever-blessed morn; etc.

4 'As we watched at dead of night,
Lo, we saw a wondrous light;
Angels singing "Peace on earth"
Told us of the Saviour's birth':

Hail, thou ever-blessed morn; etc.

5 Sacred infant, all divine,
What a tender love was thine,
Thus to come from highest bliss
Down to such a world as this:

Hail, thou ever-blessed morn; etc.

6 Teach, O teach us, holy Child,
By thy face so meek and mild,
Teach us to resemble thee,
In thy sweet humility:

Hail, thou ever-blessed morn; etc.

191 THE CHRISTMAS TREE
CHRISTBAUM
(CHRISTMAS)

Peter Cornelius
Tr. H. N. Bate

Peter Cornelius

1. The hol - ly's up, the house is all bright, The tree is rea - dy, the can - dles a - light: Re - joice _____ and be glad, _____ all child - - ren _____ to - night!

as she sings, Bend low, and an - gels touch their strings: With

'Glo - - ry' they hail the King ___ of kings. 4. The

child - ren lis - ten - ing round the tree Can hear the heav'n - ly

min - strel - sy, The man - - - ger's mar - - vel

For German text and editorial note see overleaf.

191   *CHRISTBAUM*

P. Cornelius   Ibid.

WIE schön geschmückt der festliche Raum!
Die Lichter funkeln am Weihnachtsbaum!
O fröhliche Zeit—o seliger Traum!

2 Die Mutter sitzt in der Kinder Kreis;
Nun schweiget Alles auf ihr Geheiss:
Sie singet des Christkind's Lob und Preis.

3 Und rings, vom Weihnachtsbaum erhellt
Ist schön in Bildern aufgestellt
Des heiligen Buches Palmenwelt.

4 Die Kinder schauen der Bilder Pracht
Und haben wohl des Singens acht,
Das tönt so süss in der Weihenacht!

5 O glücklicher Kreis im festlichen Raum!
O gold'ne Lichter am Weihnachtsbaum!
O fröhliche Zeit—o seliger Traum!

Carl August Peter Cornelius, nephew of the painter, Peter Cornelius, was both composer and poet; he was born at Mainz, and worked much with Liszt. Among his most famous works are the *Weihnachtslieder*, from which this carol, 'Christbaum', is taken. Cf. No. 193.

192 THE SNOW LIES THICK
(CHRISTMAS)

Selwyn Image

Geoffrey Shaw

1. The snow lies thick up-on the earth To-night, when God is come— to birth: *O col - lau - dan - tes Do - mi - num,* Let's run to give him greet - ing. His lodg-ing but a

4. But see, but see! the child's a-wake! His pret - ty hands stretch out— to take, *O col - lau - de - mus Do - mi - num,* The sim - ple gifts we bring— him: Yea, he for-gets for

417

sta - ble, see! — Where ox and ass his cour - tiers be, The
ve - ry love — The glo - ry of his home a - bove, Nor

CHORUS
f

might - y Lord — in pov - er - ty Laid low — for our — sal -
cares but on - ly this to prove, He's come — for our — sal -

Laid low, _____ laid
He's come, _____ he's

Ped.

(For verse 5 begin at letter **A**)

-va - - tion!
-va - - tion.

low — for our — sal - va - - tion!
come — for our — sal - va - - tion.

(For verse 5 begin at letter **A**)

SOPRANO SOLO

2. I hear sweet Ma - ry sing to rest_ The
3. Good Jo - seph, may we en - ter here_ To

Senza Ped.

lit - tle one a - gainst_ her breast: *O col - lau - dan - tes*
watch her and her child_ a - near, *Nos col - lau - dan - tes*

CHORUS

Ped.

SOPRANO SOLO

Do - mi - num, We'll make soft mu - sic round_them; For gen - tle as a
Do - mi - num, And kneel a - round his cra - dle? The hum - ble beasts that

Senza Ped.

419

To page 419 for v. 3
D. C. for v. 4

green   and red__ To deck a - bout his lit - tle bed, This

ve - ry God,_ who lays his head So low__ for our__ sal so
So   low,____   so

-va - tion._____
low__ for our__ sal - va - tion._____

By permission of Novello & Co. Ltd.

193 THE KINGS
DIE KÖNIGE
(EPIPHANY)

Peter Cornelius
Tr. H.N. Bate

Peter Cornelius

1. Three kings from Per - sian lands a - far To Jor-dan fol - low the point - ing star: And this the quest of the trav - el-lers three, Where the new born King of the Jews may_ be. Full roy - al gifts they bear for the King; Gold, in - cense, myrrh_ are their of - fer - ing. 2. The star shines

out___ with a stead - fast ray; The kings to Beth - le - hem make their way, And there in wor - ship they bend the_ knee, As Ma - ry's child_ in her_ lap they_ see; Their roy - al gifts they show to the King, Gold, in - cense,_ myrrh_ are their of - fer - ing.___

3. Thou child of man— lo, to Beth - le - hem

The kings are trav - 'lling— tra - vel with them!

un poco più mosso

The star of mer - cy, the star of grace, Shall lead thy—heart to its rest - ing-

P un poco più mosso

-place. Gold, in-cense, myrrh thou‿canst not‿ bring; Of-fer thy heart‿ to the

in - fant‿ King,   Of - fer   thy heart!

'Die Könige', from the *Weihnachtslieder*. The old Christmas tune 'Wie schön leuchtet' (No. 104) forms the accompaniment, and, as in Sir Ivor Atkins' well-known arrangement, may be sung by the choir.

193   *DIE KÖNIGE*

P. Cornelius   Ibid.

DREI Kön'ge wandern aus Morgenland;
Ein Sternlein führt sie zum Jordanstrand.
In Juda fragen und forschen die Drei,
Wo der neugeborene König sei?
Sie wollen Weihrauch, Myrrhen und Gold
Dem Kinde spenden zum Opfersold.

2 Und hell erglänzt des Sternes Schein;
Zum Stalle gehen die Kön'ge ein;
Das Knäblein schauen sie wonniglich,
Anbetend neigen die Kön'ge sich;
Sie bringen Weihrauch, Myrrhen und Gold
Zum Opfer dar dem Knäblein hold.

3 O Menschenkind! halte treulich Schritt!
Die Kön'ge wandern, o wandre mit!
Der Stern der Liebe, der Gnade Stern
Erhelle dein Ziel, so du suchst den Herrn,
Und fehlen Weihrauch, Myrrhen und Gold,
Schenke dein Herz dem Knäblein hold!
Schenk' ihm dein Herz!

194 KINGS IN GLORY
(CHRISTMAS: EPIPHANY)

Selwyn Image

Martin Shaw

1. Three kings in great glo - ry of hor - ses and men, Of
3. Come mon - archs, and en - ter, your Mon - arch is here, Your
5. Then sim - ple and gen - tle, and fool - ish and wise, And

hor - ses and men, In — haste come a - rid - ing o'er
Mon - arch is here, Doff — crowns, on the bare sod fall
fool - ish and wise, Come a - dore the great Lord of the

CHORUS

p

SOLO

moun - tain and fen, O'er moun - tain and fen; For their
down and re - vere, Fall down and re - vere; For the
earth and the skies, The earth and the skies, Who

Ped.   Senza Ped.

CHORUS

p

King is a - wait - ing, and lo they would bring, And
best you can of - fer is lit - tle, I trow, Is
deigns for us all on this night to be born, This

Ped.

SOLO

lo they would bring, The best of their trea - sure to
lit - tle, I trow, To the Lord God of heav'n you're a -
night to be born, This night that is fair - er than

Senza Ped.

431

195 KINGS OF ORIENT
(EPIPHANY)

Words and music by
J. H. Hopkins, Jun.
(arr. M.S.)

CASPAR
1. We three kings of O - ri - ent are; Bear - ing
5. Glo - rious now, be - hold him a - rise, King, and

MELCHIOR
1. We three kings of O - ri - ent are; Bear - ing
5. Glo - rious now, be - hold him a - rise, King, and

BALTHAZAR
1. We three kings of O - ri - ent are; Bear - ing
5. Glo - rious now, be - hold him a - rise, King, and

ACCPT.

gifts we tra - verse a - far Field and foun - tain,
God, and sac - ri - fice! Heav'n sings al - le -

gifts we tra - verse a - far Field and foun - tain,
God, and sac - ri - fice! Heav'n sings al - le -

gifts we tra - verse a - far Field and foun - tain,
God, and sac - ri - fice! Heav'n sings al - le -

moor and moun - tain, Fol - low - ing yon - der star:
-lu - ya, Al - le - lu - ya the earth re - plies:

moor and moun - tain, Fol - low - ing yon - der star:
-lu - ya, Al - le - lu - ya the earth re - plies:

moor and moun - tain, Fol - low - ing yon - der star:
-lu - ya, Al - le - lu - ya the earth re - plies:

REFRAIN (after each verse)

O_____ star of won - der, star of night,

Star with roy - al beau - ty bright, West - ward lead - ing,

still pro - ceed - ing, Guide us to thy per - fect light.

INTERLUDE

(Fl. or Ob.)

(Clar.)

MELCHIOR
2. Born   a   king   on   Beth - le - hem plain,   Gold   I

CASPAR
3. Frank - in - cense   to   of - fer have I;   In - cense

BALTHAZAR
4. Myrrh   is   mine;   its   bit - ter per - fume   Breathes   a

bring,   to   crown him   a - gain—   King   for   ev - er,

owns   a   de - i - ty nigh: Prayer   and prais - ing,

life   of   gath - er - ing gloom;   Sorrow - ing, sigh - ing,

ceas - ing nev - - er, Ov - er   us   all   to   reign:

all   men rais - - ing, Wor - ship him, God   most   high:

bleed - ing, dy - - ing, Sealed in   the   stone - cold   tomb:

For verse 5 go back to the beginning. Verses 2, 3 and 4 should be sung as solos for men's voices, the accompaniment and refrain remaining unchanged.

The verses may be sung dramatically, in a hall or in church, the three kings entering in procession as they sing the first verse. Standing together (and each holding a casket), each may turn to the people to sing his verse, all forming round an imaginary crib for the choruses and v. 5. This last verse may then be sung full, the three kings returning to their places during the last two lines of the chorus.

This carol is one of the most successful modern examples. It was both written and composed (c. 1857) by Dr. J. H. Hopkins, Rector of Christ's Church, Williamsport, Pennsylvania, who died at Troy, New York, in 1891. See his *Carols, Hymns, and Songs*, New York, 1882.

196 BLAKE'S CRADLE SONG
(GENERAL)

William Blake

R. Vaughan Williams

1. Sweet dreams, form a shade
5. Wept for me, for thee, for all,
6. Smiles on thee, on me, on all;

O'er my love-ly in-fant's head: Sweet dreams of pleas-ant streams By
When he was an in-fant small. Thou his i-mage ev-er see,—
Who be-came an in-fant small. In-fant smiles are his own smiles;—

hap-py, si-lent, moon-y beams.
Heav'n-ly face that smiles on thee,—
Heav'n and earth to peace be-guiles.

2. Sweet sleep, with soft down Weave thy brows an in - fant crown.
3. Sleep, sleep, hap - py child, All cre - a - tion slept and smiled;
4. Sweet babe, in thy face Ho - ly im - age I can trace.

Sweet sleep, an - gel mild, Hov - er o'er my hap - - py
Sleep, sleep, hap - py sleep, While o'er thee thy mo - - ther
Sweet babe, once like thee, Thy Ma - ker lay, and wept for

D.S. for vv. 5 &6

child.
weep.
me,

Words from Blake's *Songs of Innocence*, etched in 1789.

197 THE CROWN OF ROSES

(Tchaikovsky's 'Legend')

(GENERAL)

Plechtchéev, tr. G. D.

P. I. Tchaikovsky

1. When Jesus Christ was yet a child He had a garden small and wild, Wherein he cherished roses fair, And wove them into garlands there.

2. Now once, as summertime drew nigh, There came a

437

troop___ of child - ren___ by, And see - ing ro - ses on the

tree, With shouts they plucked them mer - ri - ly.

3. 'Do you bind ro - ses in___ your hair?'___ They cried, in

'Do you bind ro - ses in your hair?' They cried, in

3. 'Do you bind ro - ses in___ your hair?' They cried, in

scorn, to Je - sus there.___ The boy said hum - bly: 'Take, I pray, All but the nak - ed thorns a - way.' 4. Then of the

thorns they made a crown, And with rough fin - gers pressed it

down, Till on his fore - head fair and young Red drops of

blood like ro - ses sprung.

like ro - ses sprung, like ro - ses sprung.

The Russian composer, Peter Ilich Tchaikovsky, was born in 1840 and died at St. Petersburg in 1893. From his *Chansons pour la Jeunesse*, Moscow, 1883: Plechtchéev wrote the words, which were translated into German by Hans Schmidt. The melody is used by Arensky in his *Variations on a Theme by Tchaikovsky*

THE CAROLS ARRANGED
FOR USE THROUGHOUT THE YEAR

Titles are printed in italic, and when the beginning of the first line is used as a title, this part is printed in italic.

The carols classed under the heading *Nativity* are suitable for Christmas, but can also be sung in church at any time outside Lent throughout the year. On more informal occasions the Christmas carols themselves can sometimes be sung outside the Christmas season. The danger can thus be lessened of many beautiful Christmas carols being never sung, and the spirit of Christmas can be more widely diffused.

ADVENT
(*For the Fourth Sunday, see also* Christmas Eve)

5	*The Praise of Christmas.* All hail to the days
134	*If ye would hear* the angels sing
115	*Joseph and Mary.* O, Joseph being an old man truly
133	*Carol of the Advent.* People, look East
114	*No Room in the Inn.* When Caesar Augustus
41	*Righteous Joseph.* When righteous Joseph wedded was

CHRISTMAS EVE
(*Also for Christmas*)

123	*Chanticleer.* All this night shrill chanticleer
66	*The Cherry Tree Carol.* (*Part* 2) As Joseph was a-walking
168	*Ben Jonson's Carol.* I sing the birth was born tonight
134	*If ye would hear* the angels sing
138	*O Little Town* of Bethlehem
189	*Merry Christmas.* On Christmas Eve the bells were rung
24	*Sussex Carol.* On Christmas night all Christians sing
1	*Christmas Eve.* The Lord at first did Adam make

CHRISTMAS
From the week before Christmas to February 2nd
(*See also under* Nativity)

116	*A Babe is Born* all of a may
73	*Dutch Carol.* A child is born in Bethlehem
2	*A Child this Day* is born
118	*Susanni.* A little child there is yborn
74	*Flemish Carol.* A little child on the earth
4	*A Virgin most Pure,* as the prophets do tell
169	*Tyrley, Tyrlow.* About the field they piped full right
5	*The Praise of Christmas.* All hail to the days
119	*Angels, from the Realms* of glory
3	*Sunny Bank.* As I sat on a sunny bank (I saw three ships)
170	*New Prince, new pomp.* Behold a simple tender babe
6	*Irish Carol.* Christmas Day is come
7	*Hereford Carol.* Come all you faithful Christians
8	*Somerset Carol.* Come all you worthy gentlemen
10	*Come, love we God!*
154	*Courons à la fête*
135	*Earthly Friends* will change and falter
76	*Es ist ein' Ros'* entsprungen
186	*Snow in the Street.* From far away we come to you
11	*God rest you merry,* gentlemen
12	*God rest you merry* gentlemen (*London*)
13	*God's Dear Son* without beginning
14	*Wexford Carol.* Good people all
111	*Grand Dieu! Que de merveilles*
67	*Song of the Nuns of Chester.* He who made the starry skies
18	*I saw Three Ships* come sailing in
168	*Ben Jonson's Carol.* I sing the birth was born tonight
117	*Immortal Babe,* who this dear day
120	*In Bethlehem, that fair City*
75	*Bethlehem.* In that poor stable
187	*Mid-Winter.* In the bleak mid-winter
17	*All in the Morning.* It was on Christmas Day

162 *Je sais, vierge Marie*
77 *Song of the Crib.* Joseph dearest, Joseph mine
140 *Laissez paître vos bêtes*
20 *Yeoman's Carol.* Let Christians all with joyful mirth
23 *Make we joy* now in this feast
137 *Masters in this Hall*
149 *Noël nouvelet,* Noël chantons ici
147 *Nous allons, ma mie*
188 *Our Brother is Born.* Now every child that dwells on earth
173 *The Golden Carol.* Now is Christèmas ycome
115 *Joseph and Mary.* O, Joseph being an old man truly
138 *O Little Town* of Bethlehem
22 *Coventry Carol.* O sisters too
121 *Falan-tiding.* Out of the orient crystal skies
78 *Personent Hodie* voces puerulae
166 *Promptement levez-vous,* mon voisin
164 *Quelle est cette odeur agréable?*
79 *Quem Pastores* laudavere
67 *Song of the Nuns of Chester.* Qui creavit coelum
144 *Quittez, Pasteurs*
25 *A Gallery Carol.* Rejoice and be merry
42 *Remember,* O thou man (*verses* 1, 3, 4, 5, 6)
190 *Winter's Snow.* See amid the winter's snow
79 *Quem Pastores.* Shepherds left their flocks a-straying
133 *Shepherds, shake off your drowsy sleep*
78 *Personent Hodie.* Sing aloud on this day!
27 *The First Nowell* the angel did say
191 *The Christmas Tree.* The holly's up, the house is all bright
192 *The Snow lies thick* upon the earth
76 *Es ist ein' Ros'.* There is a flower springing
29 *This New Christmas Carol*
81 *Torches,* torches
156 *Une vaine crainte* trouble vos esprits
174 *Welcome Yule,* thou merry man
122 *Herrick's Carol.* What sweeter music can we bring
33 *While Shepherds Watched* their flocks by night
82 *Patapan.* Willie, take your little drum
83 *Congaudeat.* With merry heart let all

CHRISTMAS, Secular
171 *Shakespeare's Carol.* Blow, blow thou winter wind
50 *Nos Galan.* Deck the hall with boughs of holly
16 *Good-bye.* God bless the master of this house
15 *Wassail Song.* Here we come a-wassailing
172 *Make we merry,* both more and less
189 *Merry Christmas.* On Christmas Eve the bells were rung
19 *Boar's Head Carol.* The boar's head in hand bear I
32 *Somerset Wassail.* Wassail, and wassail, all over the town!
31 *Gloucestershire Wassail.* Wassail, wassail, all over the town!
21 *Sir Christèmas.* Who is there that singeth so

ST. STEPHEN (December 26th)
136 *Good King Wenceslas* looked out
26 *Saint Stephen* was a holy man
174 *Welcome Yule,* thou merry man

ST. JOHN (December 27th)
174 *Welcome Yule,* thou merry man

INNOCENTS' DAY (December 28th)
120 *In Bethlehem, that fair City*
22 *Coventry Carol.* O sisters too
55 *The Miraculous Harvest.* Rise up, rise up, you merry men all
80 *Three Kings* are here
92 *Puer nobis.* Unto us a boy is born!
174 *Welcome Yule,* thou merry man
140 *The Band of Children.* What songs are these, faint heard and far?

NEW YEAR
(*cf.* Christmas)

JANUARY AND FEBRUARY
(*cf.* Epiphany, Candlemas, etc.)

EPIPHANY
January 6th to Septuagesima

NATIVITY
(*Suitable both for Christmas and for General use*)

66 *The Cherry Tree Carol.* (*Part* 3) Then Mary took
197 *The Crown of Roses.* When Jesus Christ was yet a child
72 *Wondrous Works.* (*Part* 2) When they bereaved his life

PALM SUNDAY
(*cf.* Passiontide)
146 *The Merchants' Carol.* As we rode down

HOLY WEEK AND GOOD FRIDAY
See Passiontide

EASTERTIDE
Easter Day till Ascension Day
(*cf.* Spring)
71 *My Dancing Day.* (*Part* 3) Before Pilate the Jews me brought
147 *Easter Carol.* Cheer up, friends and neighbours
148 *Christ the Lord is risen!*
94 *Easter Eggs*
102 *Gabriel's Message* does away
104 *How Brightly Beams* the morning star!
152 *Festival Carol.* How great the harvest is
71 *My Dancing Day.* (*Part* 2) Into the desert I was led
17 *All in the Morning.* (*Part* 2) It was on Holy Wednesday
95 *Now glad of Heart* be every one!
149 *Love is come again.* Now the green blade riseth
35 *Sans Day Carol.* Now the holly bears a berry
96 *Hilariter.* The whole bright world rejoices now
150 *The World Itself* keeps Easter Day
97 *The Secret Flower.* This child was born
151 *Athens.* 'Twas about the dead of night
72 *Wondrous Works.* (*Part* 2) When they bereaved

ASCENSIONTIDE
71 *My Dancing Day.* (*Part* 3) Before Pilate the Jews me brought
127 *God is Ascended* up on high
152 *Festival Carol.* How great the harvest is
95 *Now glad of Heart* be every one!
72 *Wondrous Works.* (*Part* 2) When they bereaved

WHITSUNTIDE
And the Holy Spirit
59 *Welsh Carol.* Awake were they only
152 *Festival Carol.* How great the harvest is
97 *The Secret Flower.* This child was born
153 *Song of the Spirit.* When Christ blessed his disciples
154 *The Spirit.* Winds of God unfailing

TRINITY SUNDAY
(*cf.* General: Praise)
152 *Festival Carol.* How great the harvest is
95 *Now glad of Heart* be every one!
96 *Hilariter.* The whole bright world rejoices now

OTHER FESTIVAL OCCASIONS
(*cf.* General: Praise)
Saints' Days
100 *The Message.* A message came to a maiden young
156 *Summer Time.* Lift your hidden faces
132 *Psalm of Sion.* O mother dear, Jerusalem
97 *The Secret Flower.* This child was born
99 *Flower Carol* (*verses* 3, 4, 5). Through each wonder

Dedication, etc.
162 *Bell Carol.* In every town and village
44 *The Lamb of God.* (*Part* 2) It was early (*Missionary, etc.*)
88 *Waking-Time.* Neighbour, what was the sound, I pray (*Missionary, etc.*)
111 *The Builders.* Sing, all good people gathered
139 *Infinite Light.* The greatness of God (*Missionary, etc.*)
121 *Falan-tiding.* The wise may bring their learning
166 *Carol of Service.* Up, my neighbour, come away (*Missionary, etc.*)

THE CAROLS ARRANGED

SPRING
126   *Candlemas Eve*. Down with the rosemary and bays
155   *April*. Now April has come
 98   *Spring has come*. Now the spring has come again
129   *Pleasure it is*
 99   *Flower Carol*. Spring has now unwrapped the flowers
 96   *Hilariter*. The whole bright world rejoices now

MAY
 47   *May Carol*. Awake, awake, good people all
 48   *May-Day Garland*. I've brought you here a bunch of may!
 49   *Furry Day Carol*. Remember us poor Mayers all!

SUMMER
101   *Gems of Day*. All the gay gems of day
156   *Summer Time*. Lift your hidden faces
128   *Welcome, Summer*. Now welcome, Summer, with thy sunnè soft
129   *Pleasure it is*
157   *Summer Carol*. The dawn-wind now is waking
 96   *Hilariter*. The whole bright world rejoices now

HARVEST
158   *Thanksgiving Carol*. Fields of corn, give up your ears
129   *Pleasure it is*
159   *Golden Sheaves*. Sing to the Lord of harvest

AUTUMN
158   *Thanksgiving Carol*. Fields of corn, give up your ears
 63   *Green grow'th the Holly*
 38   *The Holly and the Ivy*

WINTER
 63   *Green grow'th the Holly*
 50   *Nos Galan*. Now the joyful bells a-ringing
133   *Carol of the Advent*. People, look East

GENERAL
(*Carols classed under* Nativity *are also suitable for general use*)
100   *The Message*. A message came to a maiden young
101   *Gems of Day*. All the gay gems of day
 51   *The Sinners' Redemption*. All you that are to mirth inclined
 57   *Dives and Lazarus*. As it fell out upon one day
 58   *Jacob's Ladder*. As Jacob with travel
 59   *Welsh Carol*. Awake were they only
 60   *Job*. Come all you worthy Christian men
  9   *Dark the Night* lay
161   *The Shepherd*. Down in the valley
 61   *Down in yon Forest*
103   *The Birds*. From out of a wood
102   *Gabriel's Message* does away
 63   *Green grow'th the Holly*
104   *How Brightly Beams* the morning star!
145   I know a lovely angel-game
162   *Bell Carol*. In every town and village
163   *The Three Traitors*. It was about the deep of night
 17   *All in the Morning*. It was on Christmas Day
 65   *The Decree*. Let Christians all with one accord rejoice
165   *Paen (Part 2)*. Lift up your heads
105   *The Garden of Jesus*. Lord Jesus hath a garden
131   *Coverdale's Carol*. Now blessed be thou
106   *So, Brother*. Now, brothers, lift your voices
108   *The Kingdom*. O, I have seen a King's new baby
109   *O Little One* sweet
132   *Psalm of Sion*. O mother dear, Jerusalem
181   *Balulalow*. O my dear heart
184   *All Bells in Paradise*. Over yonder's a park
111   *The Builders*. Sing, all good people gathered
110   *Jesus of the Manger*. Sing, good company, frank and free!
 69   *The Saviour's Work*. The babe in Bethlem's manger laid

70   *Joys Seven.* The first good joy that Mary had
139 *Infinite Light.* The greatness of God
46   *The Bellman's Song.* The moon shines bright
165 *Golden Mornings.* They saw the light
68   *The Truth from Above.* This is the truth sent from above
112 *Eia, Eia.* To us in Bethlem city
71   *My Dancing Day.* Tomorrow shall be
166 *Carol of Service.* Up, my neighbour, come away
64   *A New Dial.* (*In those twelve days.*) What are they
72   *Wondrous Works.* When Jesus Christ was twelve years' old
197 *The Crown of Roses.* When Jesus Christ was yet a child
167 *Carol of the Kingdom.* When Jesus was a baby
41   *Righteous Joseph.* When righteous Joseph wedded was
154 *The Spirit.* Winds of God unfailing

GENERAL, Cradle Songs
(*cf.* Nativity *for Cradle Songs of the Nativity*)
130 *Watts's Cradle Song.* Hush! my dear
185 *Wither's Rocking Hymn.* Sweet baby, sleep!
196 *Blake's Cradle Song.* Sweet dreams, form a shade

GENERAL, Legendary
53   *The Carnal and the Crane.* As I passed by a river-side
56   *The Holy Well.* As it fell out one May morning
163 *The Three Traitors.* It was about the deep of night
66   *The Cherry Tree Carol.* Joseph was an old man
55   *The Miraculous Harvest.* Rise up, rise up, you merry men all
54   *King Herod and the Cock.* There was a star in David's land
197 *The Crown of Roses.* When Jesus Christ was yet a child

GENERAL, Medieval
180 *Adam lay ybounden*
52   *Angelus ad Virginem*
62   *All and Some.* Exortum est in love
182 *Lullay my Liking.* I saw a fair maiden
183 *I sing of a Maiden*
177 *Out of your Sleep* arise and wake

GENERAL, Praise
160 *Angels Holy*, high and lowly
152 *Festival Carol.* How great the harvest is
165 *Golden Mornings* (*verses* 3, 4). O every thought be of his grace
107 *Praise to God* in the highest!
164 *Carol of Beauty.* Praise we the Lord
99   *Flower Carol* (*verses* 3, 4, 5). Through each wonder

SUITABLE FOR USE IN PROCESSION
2   *A Child this Day* is born. (*Christmas*)
4   *A Virgin most Pure.* (*Christmas*)
119 *Angels, from the Realms of glory.* (*Christmas*)
160 *Angels Holy*, high and lowly. (*General*)
152 *Festival Carol.* How great the harvest is. (*Easter to Trinity*)
17   *All in the Morning.* It was on Christmas Day (*Christmas to Easter*)
105 *The Garden of Jesus.* Lord Jesus hath a garden. (*General, and Saints*)
137 *Masters in this Hall.* (*Christmas*)
173 *The Golden Carol.* Now is Christèmas ycome. (*Christmas*)
111 *The Builders.* Sing, all good people gathered. (*General, and Dedication*)
27   *The First Nowell* the angel did say (*Christmas*)
192 *The snow lies thick* upon the earth. (*Christmas*)
194 *Kings in Glory.* Three kings in great glory. (*Epiphany*)

For Conclusions of Services or Concerts, see Praise; *also the following verses:* 16 *Good-bye,* 44 (*Pt.* 3), *Good Wishes*; 45 (4-6), *Sussex Mummers*; 49 (6), *Furry Day*; 99 (5), *Flower Carol*; 104 (3), *How brightly*; 129, *Pleasure it is*; 152 (4, 5), *Festival Carol*; 165 (*Pt.* 2), *Paean*; etc.

NOTES ON THE USE OF CAROLS

THE following notes are the result of consultation and experiment.

Waits customarily sing during the week before Christmas. Properly organized from good choirs, they might supplant the casual choir-boys and sturdy but unmusical beggars who are a nuisance at so many front doors. Waits may be accompanied by wind instruments, but harmoniums are as fatal to carols as to hymns. It is often worth while to announce the day and the district beforehand, together with a charity to which the money will be given after expenses have been deducted.

Carol Parties. Sometimes a dozen or two men and women from a choral society visit people by arrangement in their own houses, the host inviting a party to listen to carols for an hour, and making a small contribution to a charity. A whole round of half-hour parties can be managed by car on Christmas Eve.

Private Houses and Schools. There is often amateur carol singing in private houses and at school breaking-up parties. But sometimes on such occasions nearly all the carols sung are poor imitations: amateur singers and school teachers need the warning that strong commercial interests are engaged in pushing inferior songs of all descriptions; and the true carol is still obscured by the false, because the nature of carols has not been fully understood. The simplest remedy is to choose from the traditional tunes.

Concert Rooms and Parish Halls. No concerts are so popular as those which consist of carols. Since crowded audiences are assured, it is worth while to obtain the best musical help and to pay professional musicians, and local orchestras and bands. Such concerts can be made even more delightful by interspersing two or three carols sung dramatically (*e.g.* Nos. 20, 26, 48, 49, 64, 77, 88, 90, 173, 195). Costume can also be used; and in any case it is perhaps best to avoid evening clothes. Some may come on as a party of waits to sing carols like Nos. 15, 30, 31. Carol concerts need not be only in the period between Advent Sunday and Septuagesima: Lent, Easter and Spring carol concerts should, for instance, be very popular.

In Church. Groups of carols, both during and after a service, are a good way of marking Easter and other festivals as well as Christmas.

In some churches carols are sung on Easter Day and other festivals instead of an evening sermon. On ordinary Sundays appropriate carols would form a sound and very popular substitute for anthems in many churches.

Children's Services. It has been found a good plan to sing a carol to the children on any Sundays throughout the year when a good singer can be got.

Carol Services. We suggest a new type of informal popular service, to be announced as a 'Carol Service', and to be held on every Sunday throughout the year, in the afternoon, or in the evening. The name will at once attract; and, if the music chosen is really carol music, the whole service will have a delightful character. We suggest that this Carol Service should last from one hour to an hour and a quarter, but not longer; and that it should take something like the following form:—

1 Short Prayer; 2 Hymn or Carol: 3 First Reading; 4 Carol A; 5 Poetry; 6 Carol B; 7 Notices; 8 Carol C; 9 Second Reading; 10 Carol D; 11 Short Lecture or Address; 12 Hymn or Carol; 13 Lord's Prayer and Grace.

In this scheme, perhaps the carols marked A and B might be in the main for a choir or quartet, and those numbered C and D of a more congregational character. If carols are sung for Nos. 2 and 12, the people's share would be further increased. Should still more carols be wanted, a solo carol might be substituted sometimes for No. 5, or for some other number. The First Reading in this example is from the Bible, the Second is from some other source, as a rule. All the readings and other parts are meant to be short—about the length of the Gospels in the Prayer Book. It has been found that improvised versicles and responses have a remarkable effect upon the general tone of these gatherings; they may be taken from the carol itself, announced when it is given out, and then repeated by the person in charge and the people before the carol is sung. Sometimes the refrain can be thus used, sometimes the opening lines, sometimes another couplet from the carol. The congregation can also be brought in by some verses being allotted to them, as well as by their joining in the choruses.

INDEX OF COMPOSERS, SOURCES, ETC.

(There are sometimes two traditional tunes to one number.)

INDEX OF AUTHORS, SOURCES, ETC.

(The word 'Traditional' may cover any date or era
from the fifteenth to the eighteenth century)

INDEX OF TITLES

INDEX OF TITLES

451

INDEX OF FIRST LINES